ROB.
1608 N. FELL
BLOOMINGTON, ILL. 61701

The Voice
of Illness

Aarne Siirala

The Voice of Illness

A Study in Therapy and Prophecy

Foreword by
PAUL TILLICH

Introduction by
GOTTHARD BOOTH, M.D.

FORTRESS PRESS   PHILADELPHIA

© 1964 by Fortress Press

Library of Congress Catalog Card Number 64-10647

Printed in the United States of America

Grateful acknowledgment is made to the following publishers
for permission to use copyrighted material: EVZ-Verlag, Zurich;
Harcourt, Brace & World, Inc.; LIVERIGHT; The Macmillan
Company; W. W. Norton & Company, Inc.; Oxford University
Press; Philosophical Library, Inc.; The University of Chicago
Press; Wesleyan University; The Westminster Press.

The quoted material on pp. 94, 100, 103, and 104 is from
Studies in Hysteria by Joseph Breuer and Sigmund Freud, au-
thorized translation by Dr. A. A. Brill. Copyright 1937 by the
Nervous and Mental Disease Publishing Company. This copyright was renewed in 1950 by the Nervous and Mental Disease
Publishing Company; and the beneficial interest therein resides
in the Brill Trust. Reprinted by permission.

6745A64   UB958

Foreword

Dr. Aarne Siirala's book *The Voice of Illness* is an important link in the ever-increasing number of writings which deal positively with the relation of religion to psychotherapy and medicine in general. The very title of the book is significant. If illness has a voice it tries to say something to us, and one main intention of this book is to tell us what it is saying, namely that illness itself is not only something negative but rather an indication of a profound negativity; its own message is the first step in the conquest of illness. It is, above all, the distorted relation between the individual and the social group to which illness points. Therefore healing is a restitution of an integrated relationship to the social group. The means of communication is the word, and this leads to a very interesting discussion of the healing power of the word, both the word of man and the divine Word. If sickness is seen in this way it may well be that it is a healthy reaction against a sick society. Disease therefore becomes highly ambiguous and can be evaluated both negatively and positively.

Such considerations agree with the universal character of life, i.e., the ambiguity between creative and destructive forces. The same event can show both characteristics. Of course the question remains: How can a seemingly meaningless disease—feeble-mindedness, for instance, or the diseases of children who die in early infancy—be justified? In such cases it is hard to hear the voice of illness. The voice then can only say something about the universal structure of estranged life in time and space. It can only say something about the negativity and possible positivity of the universe, but in this sense the voice of illness transcends both individuality and community.

It is theologically important that a book such as this one show the intimate relationship between healing and salvation. The original meaning of the word "salvation" is healing, and it is one of the important contributions of Dr. Siirala's book that he brings together the word as the means of healing with the Word as the means of salvation and in this way combines the medical and the theological interpretations of human existence. It is certainly impossible for us to understand salvation in terms of saving from hell and elevating to heaven unless these two concepts are understood highly symbolically. Salvation must be understood as healing in the ultimate dimension, which includes directly or indirectly all other dimensions of human existence. Medical healing, including psychotherapy, in this view is a part of salvation but of course not the final salvation because in itself it does not heal the split between the temporal order in which we live and the eternal to which we belong.

Dr. Siirala's book is a serious and important contribution to theology, for theology today is not permitted to repeat the traditional formulations. It must understand what salvation means, and I do not believe that this can be understood without an understanding of what healing means. The way in which Dr. Siirala shows the relation of the two is important not only for the doctrine of man but also for a theological understanding of the drama of salvation.

PAUL J. TILLICH

The University of Chicago
Chicago, Illinois
October 1, 1963

Preface

The Voice of Illness—in both its Finnish and English forms—was written during my appointment as Visiting Scholar at Union Theological Seminary, New York City, 1960-63. It is with deep gratitude that I recall the inspiration and guidance given to me by the faculty of that seminary.

During my residence in New York City I maintained stimulating contact with many distinguished representatives of the medical and psychiatric professions. In this connection it is important to mention the names of Dr. Gotthard Booth, Dr. Harold Kelman, and Dr. John W. R. Thompson, all of whom showed especial interest in my research.

Director Paul Chapman of The Packard Manse, Stoughton, Massachusetts, and Professor Taito A. Kantonen of Hamma Divinity School, Wittenberg University, Springfield, Ohio, both aided in preparing the English edition of this book.

Finally, let me record my enduring appreciation to Professor Paul J. Tillich of The University of Chicago and Dr. Gotthard Booth of New York City for their interest in my work and for their gracious willingness to contribute substantially to this volume.

AARNE SIIRALA

Waterloo Lutheran University
Waterloo, Ontario, Canada
September, 1963

Contents

Chapter 3

THE THERAPEUTIC ENCOUNTER WITH ILLNESS

Chapter 4

THERAPY AND PROPHECY

x

Introduction

The Voice of the Body

by GOTTHARD BOOTH, M.D.

The Body as Symbol

The Voice of Illness deals with the form of illness which expresses itself through the medium of language. The gift of words, although potentially the instrument of reason, is all too often misused to make man "more bestial than any beast" (Goethe, *Faust,* I). Contradictions between the letter and the spirit, between language and existence, are inherent in psychological illness. As the latter ranges from the "normal" problems of life to the extremes of insanity, it constantly challenges both ministers and psychiatrists to work for psychological health. Yet the inevitable ambiguity of words creates complications in the shared labors of medicine and theology, for each thinker in these disciplines has his own language with its explicit and implicit values. Since psychological illness expresses itself specifically in words, the nature of illness as such is obscured in the realm of psychiatry. Dr. Siirala has therefore asked me to discuss the phenomenon of illness as it expresses itself in the human body.

Mankind has known intuitively since early times that the body speaks a very basic and very honest language through the healthy and unhealthy functioning of its organs. Our expressive gestures, the color of our skin, and the behavior of our heart and our bowels, of our lungs and our genitals, unequivocally spell out our existential situation. The lie detector, reading the body directly, triumphs over the faculty of words to hide the truth. As Ludwig Klages, the

1

founder of scientific graphology, described the relationship: "The body is the expression of the soul, the soul is the meaning of the body." In the course of the past forty years scientific research has accumulated more and more evidence that this intuitive insight is correct.

More important than the mass of empirical material, however, is the theoretical insight into the lawful nature of the relationship between body and mind, an insight made particularly clear in the work of F. S. Rothschild (24)* who applied the principles of semantics to the evolution of life. Retracing life's stages from the organization of the human brain back to the amoeba, he classified all physical structures in their role as carriers of specific forms of communication between subject and object. Each organ not only supports the life of the body, but also serves a specific relationship between body and environment. The different forms of the nose in the bulldog, the anteater and the elephant are obvious examples, but the principle also is responsible for differing brain structure in such mammals as the porpoise and the horse. Both the appearance and the inner anatomy of an organism reflect its place in the context of nature and are therefore symbols of its specific life in the same way a wheel is a symbol of motion or a letter of a certain sound.

The meaning of an organ and its functions always transcends its physical elements, just as the meaning of a word transcends the letters which compose it or the meaning of a sentence transcends the words which compose it. The growing complexity of organisms in the course of evolution is the expression of an expanding range of communication between subjects and objects. The intricate structure of the brain of the higher mammals represents the syntax which organizes these manifold interrelationships into rational patterns. For the needs of man, however, the brain has proved inadequate. He has developed a system of nonbiological

---

* Numbers in parentheses refer to the works listed on pp. 24-25.

structures of communication, language, which enables him to interpret and control the levels of prehuman communication which are expressed only through bodily forms and organ functions and which have remained the biological foundation of human existence.

When the human organism is seen in this light it is understandable that the language of the body is straightforward and unequivocal in contrast to words. The syntax of the body has been structurally fixed since prehistoric times; language proper, on the other hand, is still in flux. Nothing illustrates this point better than the King James Version of the Bible. Although it has stayed a living part of English literature for the past 350 years, its message can no longer be completely understood by the modern reader, because many of its words and usages have either disappeared from contemporary English or have radically changed in meaning. This is not true of the word "illness," which still has the same general meaning. When we come to the problem of defining "psychological illness," however, we immediately get lost in the quicksands of the idiosyncratic use of words which Siirala discusses in this book. Illness has an unequivocal meaning only in the context of the body. In the context of verbal communication the same description of an experience may be regarded by some as a sign of spiritual health and by others as a symptom of a mind out of touch with "reality" or God. A physical symptom, however, always has the same immutable meaning in the communication between the individual and the world. *In the state of illness the person is alienated from the object of the affected function* (4). One may describe physical disease as insanity of the body. This purely negative formulation is inadequate, since even a psychotic process does not annul the individual personality, but only disturbs communication with others. The body always expresses the soul, in illness as much as in health. One may even say that illness expresses the soul more impressively than health in the same way that a good caricature expresses essential aspects of a personality more clearly than photographs taken in uncharacteristic situations.

Illness as Alienation

The essential character of disease is illustrated most clearly in the dramatic event of an epileptic attack. In a moment the patient makes the transition from normal social relatedness to an unconscious state in which the whole organism concentrates on the convulsions of the motoric system. After the storm has exhausted its fury, consciousness and normal rapport with the environment are re-established. This sequence of events defines a specific personality type: a person endowed with both a strong tendency toward aggression and the capacity to control it ordinarily, subordinating it to constructive social behavior. Only an intolerable accumulation of aggressive tensions can occasionally overwhelm the conscious personality to such an extent that the tensions are discharged in the form of socially harmless fits. In the rare cases when an epileptic has committed murder, he has done so while unconscious. The accumulation of aggressive tension is visibly dependent on events in the life of the epileptic. For example, I once saw a ward patient go into a seizure while he was signing his name to a birthday card for his brother, the oldest son of the family. Consciously he had accepted the fact that the brother had inherited the family farm, but to carry goodness to the point of celebrating his brother's birthday proved too irritating to be confined within conventional behavior. The seizure expressed a compromise between respect for the brother's personality and the need at least symbolically to act out the aggressive impulse.

The contrast in the epileptic personality between generally overcontrolled healthy behavior and the evident violence of the fit earned epilepsy the name *morbus sacer* in antiquity. A demon seemed to take possession of the body. It was Hippocrates who introduced the notion that epilepsy is a disease like any other, the result of "natural causes." His causal interpretation was not so much of an advance in the theory of disease as it may appear at first sight. The father of rational medicine retained the primitive concept that external agents overwhelm the victim and harm his body. Even today, physical injuries, chemical substances, bacteria, and viruses are considered enemies of man ready to take advantage of any neglect in the defensive system of the body, no different in character from the demons of old. Diseases have assumed individual characters in Western medicine. Science has delighted in naming each frequent combination of symptoms as if it belonged to some mysterious organism—epilepsy, tuberculosis, cancer, etc.— each as if it had its own natural history and would have its own way with the patients unless they could fight it off. Are such national campaigns as "Fight cancer" and "Fight tuberculosis" really more scientific, more sophisticated in spirit, than the exorcistic rituals of ancient medicine men? As Freud discovered, and Siirala documents in the present book, the Inquisitors were well informed about "witches" from the point of view of disease description; they were only mistaken in their interpretations. They argued very logically and very simply that every event must have a cause, and that an evil event must be caused by a power hostile to the victim: the devil.

Modern medicine has followed this line of thinking; it has gone all out in tracking down "disease demons" which have one thing in common: they are all defined as something destructive which attacks the otherwise healthy body in the form of bad genes, birth injuries, faults of nutrition, germs, toxic substances, etc. Psychoanalysis has added various forms of damage which civilization, specifically religious moralism, inflicts on the "normal instincts" which seek oral, anal, and sexual gratifications. It is not difficult to see that the underlying concept of man as "naturally healthy" represents a Manichean dualism of good and evil as warring cosmic powers. Careful observation of sick persons reveals, however, that the negative aspect of illness, the reduction of the affected function, does not exhaust the significance of sickness. The example of the epileptic attack showed more than an unconscious man, his muscles given over to useless thrashing around. It showed an episode in the life of a man who practices self-control to such an extent that he expresses his capacity for rage only in symbolic form. The biological function is used as a mere gesture, but *a gesture which realistically affirms a social attitude.*

Illness as Communication

The interpretation of organic disease as *social communication* may appear strange to many readers who have been subjected to the concept of communication as a function which serves individual interests. The popular notions of life in the raw employ clichés like "struggle for survival," "self-preservation," "sexual hunger," and "cruelty of nature." They represent a narrow and tendentious selection from the life of subhuman nature and from so-called primitive human cultures, a selection of more or less correct observations which can be used to rationalize the individualistic mores of modern industrial man. Scientific observers have established clear evidence that Darwin's observations about the utilitarian bias of "natural selection" cover only part of the complexity of nature. *Social organization* of life and quasi-artistic *self-expression in the service of communication* are actually as much an integral part of biological forms as self-preservation. As Spitz (26) demonstrated clearly, even the best physical care of bodily needs does not keep a baby alive unless it is related to a mothering human being. Harlow (14, 15) has added the observation that rhesus monkeys can be kept alive if the warmth and softness of a maternal body is replaced by a dummy to which the baby can cling. Nevertheless such babies grow up into defective adults: they are incapable of carrying out the sexual act because they have not developed the function of interaction with another organism. The *gestures* "Yes" and "No" are patterned by the reflex activities of the baby which take place when the baby has found the nipple and when it has failed to find it, respectively (27). As far as body *forms* are concerned, the predominance of self-expressive over self-preserving needs is seen most strikingly in the fact that on the highest level of evolution the testicles have left the protection of the abdominal cavity. Nothing could possibly be gained for the survival of the individual or of the race by exposing the male germ cells to such danger (6, 21).

Communication between the members of the same group as well as communication with members of different symbiotic groups is thus the fundamental principle of biology. The utilitarian functions of feeding, fighting, mating, and breeding have all been used as material for the elaborate social *rituals* of animal life. The latter, like the head-nodding and the head-shaking of the human infant, are forms of symbolic communication by means of the body. They are apt to replace effectively the need for physical action on the object. In many animal species fights between rivals are ceremonial in character and do not seek the death of the vanquished. As a great animal ethologist formulated it, the end of purposive behavior is not the attainment of the object, but the performance of the consummatory action: "Not the litter or the food is the animal striving towards, but the performance itself of the maternal activities or eating" (30). Self-preservation, in other words, is a by-product of the activities of the organism. Under normal circumstances all organisms, not only man, feed and fight in their characteristic ways as an expression of living, not in order to keep their own body alive as an end in itself.

In the state of illness nothing changes as far as the principle of self-expression is concerned. Illness differs from health only with respect to *the form in which the individual relates to his specific environment*. Whereas healthy behavior patterns use the body organs, social conventions, and language in a manner which establishes and maintains positive interaction with others, *the symptoms of illness serve only as self-expression*. Usually this is not understandable to others or to the patient himself, because the conscious mind is generally out of touch with the deeper self. This deeper self asserts itself in the form of illness when the existential situation frustrates a specific need of the personality. If these needs cannot be expressed in realistic, "healthy" form, symbolic organ language takes over. This is illustrated by our previous example of the epileptic. Under the average conditions of his life he is, for all practical purposes, healthy, although he is identified with his specific liability by the pattern of his brain waves and by his unconscious reaction pattern. Only when his personal problem is excessively intensified does the expression of controlled rage change from rigidity of social manners to abnormal physical behavior, the seizure. The term "abnormal" requires qualification. Every human being is capable of going into an epileptic fit, but most people do so only in reaction to extreme stimulation, e.g., as it is applied in the form of electroshock therapy. What sets the epileptic apart is his constitutional tendency to react thus extremely to situations which do not affect the majority of people in this way.

It is probably true of most diseases that they are determined decisively by specific combinations of genes. This does not mean that the genes directly cause the pathological symptoms, but that *they excessively favor the use of one normal biological potential over others.* Even the very abnormal behavior of the cancer cell represents a regression to the earliest level of life when energy was derived from fermentation rather than oxidation (32). Before examining more examples of the relation between disease and physiological functions, it is necessary to point out that constitutional dispositions must be understood as involving not only the body but also its environment. The principle that the inner and the outer world are systematically interrelated was demonstrated first by the biologist Von Uexküll. As he formulated it: "There are as many worlds as there are subjects. These subjective worlds are formed by limited numbers of spatial elements, movement patterns, time elements and qualities of content" (31). Insofar as the subjects belong to the same species, their worlds are similar but apparently, even on primitive levels, not identical. Constitutional dispositions in human beings, often inherited independently, carry the implication of certain corresponding worlds of their own. One may describe them as Von Uexküll describes animal species: "independent organisms with their own characters and extremely long durations of life."

The specific worlds of constitutional types have been analyzed and described very fully by Szondi (28). Through clinical description and through his personality test (29) he demonstrated that the difference between healthy and sick carriers of the same genes is of a quantitative nature. Epilepsy, for instance, is the most extreme form of a way of life which is concerned with the control of aggression, and the same way of life may also take a healthy form such as religious or medical vocation or fire-fighting; paranoia is an excessive development of a tendency to get involved in the personalities of others, etc. The constitutional types tend to attract each other sexually, thus perpetuating the group because the latent genes are combined in the offspring and become more effective. If it were not for this unconscious attraction of latent tendencies, some rare hereditary diseases probably would have become extinct, since the mating of the carriers due to chance encounters is statistically unlikely.

In organic diseases the differences between the constitutional types can be classified by means of the Rorschach test. The same ten standard inkblots are perceived differently by different clinical groups. This does not mean that there is no overlap; hardly any response is unique for any one group. If one evaluates all of the responses of one patient, however, it nearly always appears that the majority of his responses fit the clinical type rather than the type of the control group (2). It is self-evident that the consistency of the inner and outer world of each individual provides the conditions for a specific life-pattern. Each human being represents a mosaic of different hereditary dispositions whose dynamic influence varies according to the dominant or latent character of the specific genes. The total of these dispositions accounts for the phenomenon Freud described as "the striving of the organism to safe-

guard its own individual path toward death" (12). He gave it, because of his pessimistic outlook, the unfortunate name *Todestrieb,*
translated even more misleadingly as "death instinct." Actually
it is not death but the *way of life* which is meant. Illnesses are
part of the individual way of life; they represent the individual
mode of approach to the natural end of physical existence.

Illness and Values

The preceding remarks about illness as expression of personality
may impress the reader as mere speculative generalizations of psychoanalytic theory. To illustrate the practical importance of the
concept, a few of the most impressive examples may be described
which indicate that since prehistoric times mankind has been developing a few clearly distinguishable personality types which are
related to major forms of physical illness.

The first of these types can be traced back to the period thirty
thousand years ago when the prehistoric *hunters* left the pictorial
record of their heroic lives on the walls of caves in France and
Spain. Their pattern of culture has been preserved into the present
by primitive tribes of the Old and the New World. What distinguishes the hunters from the earlier food gatherers is their pursuit
of big game like the ancient mammoth and cave bear, the modern
elephant and buffalo. Such a daring innovation as tackling creatures of far superior physical power presupposes the evolution of
a breed of men distinguished by individual initiative and prowess.
The religions of the hunters reflect an emphasis on *personality.*
The spirit of man is experienced as transcending his physical existence; he is considered individually immortal. Leadership is exercised by men or women who feel moved by spontaneous visions
to assume the role of shamans. Their inspiration is accepted as
genuine by the tribe.

A contrasting personality type became distinguishable in the
subsequent emergence of the *planters* about ten thousand years

ago. Here survival becomes based not on the capacity to fight individually against acute threats, but on the *subordination of the
individual* to the seasonal demands made by the plants he culti-
vates. The planter community entails a carefully structured collective organization of life which must be attuned to the cosmic
order; the role of the leader himself becomes a matter of observing
laws. Not individual inspiration, but traditional ritual confers
priesthood in planter societies. The emphasis on the group is expressed in a concept of immortality which differs from that of the
hunters. Immortality is identified with the survival of the tribe in
this world rather than the survival of the individual in the spirit
realm. Nothing expresses the difference betwen hunters and planters more convincingly than the fact that ritualistic human sacrifice
has been discovered only among planters in widely separated parts
of the world. This point is further stressed by the fact that the
victims have been selected for physical perfection or for high social rank.

The preceding descriptions of the individualistic hunters and the
collectivistic planters (8) correspond in great detail to the conclusions derived from the psychological study of *the two most
frequent forms of chronic illness in the United States.* Rheumatic
diseases on the one hand and affections of the heart and the circulation on the other shared about equally in accounting for 14.5
million out of the total of 25 million persons who were found in
1937 to suffer from chronic ailments (2). The similarity between
the anthropological and the clinical findings is particularly convincing because the clinical findings were published thirteen years
before Campbell brought the anthropological ones to the attention of a wider public (8).

Rheumatic disabilities of muscles and joints affect those who
have lived in their days of health as much like the primitive hunters as modern culture allows. The members of this group are
characterized by enjoyment of physical activity for its own sake,
not for prestige or health. Their actions are motivated by the

need for individualistic self-assertion even in the face of social opposition and great odds against practical success.

Diseases of the heart and blood vessels are typical of those who,
like the planters, have been motivated by social expectations,
physical activities, whether work or competitive sports, having
been undertaken only in order to comply with outside demands.
To give two clinical illustrations: an arthritic clerk used to carry
his light briefcase "as if it were a bucket full of water." On the
other hand an arteriosclerotic clerk continued for a whole year
after the loss of his job his daily routine of going to the business
district and returning in the evening so that nobody in the neigh-
borhood would know of his social failure.

The connection between disease symptom and personality is
understandable. Since rheumatism goes with a condition of intensified muscular tension and effort, it expresses symbolically a
predominant need for action. When illness, old age, or overwhelming obstacles have defeated the self-assertion of the individual, the organ of action becomes the center of self-expression and
its pain becomes a heightened form of self-experience.

The diseases of the cardiovascular group express dependency on
the given environment because the bloodstream represents the
primordial environment of all life. The blood is a bit of encap-
sulated and developed seawater pulsing through the higher organisms even as the ocean supported the first living cells. When
internal or external conditions deprive individuals of a milieu toward which they have been primarily oriented, the organs serving
the blood circulation become diseased: the muscles in the walls of
the arteries become tense, the walls degenerate, the heart fails.
The meaning of milieu for this personality type is expressed most
drastically in cases of sudden death. Instances have been observed
both in human beings and in animals in which the heart of an organically healthy individual stopped because of panic when he
was faced with the loss of the supporting social environment—the
so-called voodoo death (23). The most frequent form of interde-

pendence between milieu and heart disease was illustrated by the
heart attack of President Eisenhower; it came at a time he felt
uncertain whether the majority of the American people wanted
him to run for re-election. After his experience of a "heartening"
popular reaction there was no recurrence for eight years (i.e., to
the time of this writing), although age is a definite factor in heart
disease.

The manifestation of the two major prehistoric value systems
in two major contemporary clinical groups is understandable, for
modern populations are derived from both hunter and planter ancestors. Each cultural group apparently inbred and developed specific gene constellations. As the research by Szondi indicates, even
in a mixed population the mutual attraction between carriers of
latent genes perpetuates specific variants of mankind. The survival
of the two types is obviously no longer based on the external ne-
cessities which favored their origin. The complex and manifold
opportunities of industrial society allow each type to select his individual world either of self-assertion or of conformity. This is
illustrated very clearly by means of the Rorschach test. Each type
selects from the ten non-representational inkblot pictures the fea-
tures which are congenial to his attitude toward the world at large,
just as a zoologist and a botanist walking together through the
woods will observe more animals or more plants, respectively.

The continued presence of the two prehistoric personality types
is very obvious in our Judeo-Christian tradition. Although the
forms of religion have developed far beyond shamanism and the
rituals of human sacrifice, the essence of both has stayed in evidence in the coexistence of prophetic individualism and priestly
conservatism. We have Moses, Jesus, and Luther who defied the
formidable powers surrounding them, but we also have our high
feast days which are synchronized with the annual rhythm of nature. Christianity as the individualistic departure from Judaism
generally emphasizes the immortality of the soul, whereas Judaism
has survived two thousand years of minority exsitence because it

has been committed since Moses to the responsibility of preserving the chosen people.

The elaboration of the two contrasting types of relationship between man and environment may have diverted attention from the feature they have in common: both have been formed by a dependency on subhuman organisms. Only those of our primitive ancestors survived who were capable of observing "religiously" the laws by which animals and plants exist. There was a great deal of identification between the hunters and their game, between the planters and their plants. That they all inflicted death on one another was part of existence. It was acceptable as a dramatic episode in a life which transcended *physical* existence. This faith was not unrealistic. Measured and tested pragmatically, the religions of the hunters and of the planters have proved themselves adequate to maintain their adherents since prehistoric times.

The emergence of technological man has added a new perspective to the relationship between way of life and liability to disease. Nature was once regarded as the awe-inspiring manifestation of a divine spirit. Survival demanded a worshipful attitude toward nature even when that attitude was intellectualized as the scientific study of natural laws. Now that modern science and industry have made it possible to interfere with the natural order to an extent beyond the imagination of previous generations, man increasingly sees himself as the conqueror of nature, and in the field of medicine, specifically as the conqueror of disease. During the past hundred years, the latter undertaking has seemed to achieve spectacular success in the war against microbes. Antisepsis, asepsis, vaccines, and chemical compounds have contributed to reducing infectious disease and extended the average life expectancy of the population. This success has been a Pyrrhic victory, however, for as more and more researchers have realized cancer is steadily increasing as the infectious diseases decrease. It has become apparent that this phenomenon is due not to the fact that more people reach the "cancer age," as was at first supposed, but rather to the fact that cancer is directly related to the antibacterial defenses of the body (20). In previous ages man lived in generally peaceful symbiosis with bacteria. Only under special circumstances, as when the body had been weakened by malnutrition, emotional frustration, or old age, did the bacteria gain the upper hand. By contrast, cancer has never been connected with any living organism. All known cancerogenic agents are either inanimate substances or viruses, which are inanimate chemicals unless they are brought into contact with living cells.

The connection between technological progress and the changing balance of infectious and cancerous diseases is not simply an unfortunate by-product of certain scientific inadequacies of medicine. The root of both developments is found in the emergence of a new personality type. The so-called conquest of nature is not the result of intellectual advance, but of a different motivation in the use of the intellect. The question has often been asked why the Greeks and the Romans did not develop industrialism, since they had the necessary scientific and intellectual sophistication. The answer is suggested by a psychological comparison between two disease groups which are representative of the old and the new type of man: tuberculosis and cancer (7).

The use of the Rorschach method, as in the previous study of individualism and collectivism, has led to the following conclusions.

In *tuberculosis* the patient's personality has been originally and predominantly directed toward the establishment of *mutual* relationships with other human beings. Such relationships can be sublimated into involvement with impersonal causes and ideals, but the striving is always toward that which is valued as much as the self. The closest biological example of this type of relatedness is obviously the sexual striving for union in which both partners are of equal importance. Psychoanalysis has described personalities in which this motivation predominates as *genital* types. Tuberculosis may be understood as the expression of a frustrated need for affectionate involvement with another person. The destructive symbiosis with the tuberculosis bacterium takes the place of an unobtainable human partner.

In *cancer* one finds that the patient has originally been concerned with the establishment of *control over objects,* in the broadest sense of the word object. Not mutuality and partnership but the security of the particular relationship valued by this individual is needed. This trait does not imply that these patients have been selfish or possessive, nor that they have necessarily been aggressive in their attitudes toward others. Many have been self-sacrificing parents, physicians, or nurses, or religious and political idealists, although in one-sided, inflexible ways. Disease strikes them when their particular object seems to have been irretrievably lost, a fact suspected since antiquity and documented abundantly in modern times by LeShan (18). Psychoanalysis has defined this personality type as the *anal* character. The designation is based upon the observation that in the psychological development of these individuals the dynamic pattern of the anal function, that is, the earliest infantile experience of controlling an inanimate object, retains particular importance. In later life the connection between the bowels and social attitudes is usually forgotten, although an unconscious association between cancer and dirt has been observed (1). This unconscious association is probably one of the causes of the widespread reluctance to consider the role of personality in the predisposition toward cancer (7, 11). The contrast between anal and genital character is well documented in the work of Freud. As a scientist he devoted himself to the study of sex as the basic life force, but as a cancer personality he could never overcome his defensive reaction to the fact that sex makes the mates interdependent. Even in one of his last essays (13) he concluded that for both male and female sex inescapably involves an injury to the individual. He assumed that both sexes unconsciously are *anxious for control* over the penis: castration fear and

penis envy are considered the "organic rock bottom of psychoanalysis."

A cancer can be understood as a symbolic substitute for the lost
object. In the earlier life of the cancer patient *the object has
played the role of an extension of the self,* even when it has been
another individual. The tumor, as an outgrowth of the body, symbolizes the lost object (7, 22). The cells of the tumor do not in-
teract with other living organisms as is the case in bacterial infection. They react to inanimate substances which become part of the
cell chemistry, changing the cell's metabolism so that the cancer
becomes independent of oxygen. Thus even on the cellular level
cancer symbolizes the autonomy which has been the predominant
aim of the patient in his days of health.

Sacrifice

The rise of cancer and the decline of infectious disease expresses
a shift to a different value system. It can be understood as parallel
to the change from a theocentric to an anthropocentric orientation
of humanity. These terms are used in a purely descriptive sense:
the concept of God implies a living being who transcends human
power and on whom man therefore depends for his own existence.
The image of God has changed in history as human awareness of
the world has changed its focus: from the large animals of the
hunters to the crops of the planters and finally to the image of
the creative power of man himself, the being with whom man can
entertain dialogue in spite of the difference in power. In all stages
of this development man has existed by virtue of his ability to subordinate his individual life to his image of the divine realm: the
hunter risked his life in contesting powerful creatures, the planter
in accepting human sacrifice, the Jew and Christian in bearing
witness against worshipers of subhuman gods.

In the preceding section it was pointed out that the secularized
descendants of religious ancestors continue to subordinate them-

selves to the old values. These values have retained a numinous quality for them. Individualists are still lamed in the contest with the superior powers of their environment; conformists are still victimized by failure of their blood circulation as they struggle to keep up with conventional standards; those needing to share emotions with other persons are still made sick by bacteria and parasites. Many of them have been made aware by doctors that their way of life is unhealthy, but they continue even though no shaman or priest can be held responsible. *Life is sacrificed for the sake of values which are natural to the individual.*

The increased life span of modern man expresses a new attitude toward physical existence. This new attitude is the result of the spreading gospel of humanism which asserts against all previous theistic concepts that man must assume full responsibility for his fate and that his physical existence is his highest good. Scientists and politicians have therefore concentrated on improving material conditions for the greatest number of people in order to preserve life for the longest possible time. These efforts have succeeded spectacularly. Whereas all classical antiquity and medieval England added only eight and twelve years respectively to the twenty years average life expectancy of prehistoric man, contemporary man has added thirty-eight years more within just the past 400 years. In other words, the threescore and ten years that formed the highest limit of natural life in biblical times is now within the reach of almost everyone.

This success story is all too often told with no mention of the price. In the periods in which man was integrated into the living forms of nature, individuals consciously or unconsciously sacrificed their lives for the sake of participating in nature's values. As the humanists asserted the superior value of the life span, they sacrificed the old values. The new values of inanimate nature as increasingly controlled by technology and science have gained ascendancy. Man as the master of nature surrounds himself more and more with inanimate objects and machines which he can manipulate and dispose of. Activities are synchronized with clocks, results are measured in money. Art has become "nonobjective" and "nonrepresentational"; medicine has accepted the ominous word "antibiotics." The "No" to symbiotic life has invaded even sexuality. The union of man and woman has turned into the use of the partner for the achievement of a sexual outlet, a purpose for which a member of one's own sex may often be preferable. Dancing, which used to express various aspects of natural sexuality, has developed into the "twist," the motions of which run counter to all directions associated with copulation. In this dance, the equality of the sexes and their independence from each other is emphasized. For many, the womb has become as expendable an organ as the appendix.

All such phenomena illustrate an estrangement from living nature which is inherent in the increase of the anal at the expense of the genital personality type. The industrial process is in many respects an elaboration of the digestive aspect of the organism: animate and inanimate parts of the world are transformed into materials which can be used for personal survival without creating new organisms. It appears therefore consistent that those who are predominantly dedicated to values inherent in self-preservation will be rewarded with longer lives, but will also transform some vital organ into a self-sufficient object. It is also consistent that the common forms of therapy in cancer rely specifically on machines and on discoveries concerning the physicochemical aspects of biology. The cancer patient in the midst of the machinery of the modern hospital is a sad postscript to the volume of more than 200 years ago in which a physician highlighted the medical aspect of the Enlightenment and humanism: *L'Homme machine* (10). The author expected that the mechanistic approach would lead to the unimpeded enjoyment of life. Experience has taught us otherwise. Machines do not enjoy themselves and to the extent man has identified himself with machines he has sacrificed the joys of his pretechnological ancestors.

Healing

Physical disease seems to teach a negative lesson, that man comes through sickness unto death by living according to his own individual nature. It is the function best endowed for life which becomes sick and causes the fall from health. We have seen that this development cannot be blamed on the environment. The individual selects his own way of relating to the environment even as he selects specific imagery from the many possibilities suggested by Rorschach's ten inkblots. This individual bias is the organic counterpart to what Kierkegaard (17) described as "sickness unto death," the will to be one's own self and to create one's own life according to a personal hierarchy of values (6).

The negative aspect of illness, however, is only part of the story. Illness also affirms positively that man lives not only on the strength of his preferred function, but also by virtue of all those functions and values he has taken for granted. No matter whether his endowment is that of a genius or of an ordinary person, physically he cannot exist unless all his organs are relating to the environment according to their purposes, in action and in dependent existence, as autonomous body and as symbiotic partner of many other organisms. Socially man is also enmeshed in many ways: no matter how individualistic he is, he must find some place in society; no matter how conformist, he must also act individually. He may be aware chiefly of his uniqueness, but he can express that uniqueness only in relation to his fellow man; he may feel only his solidarity with the group, but he must live as a person.

Illness sets the balance straight between preferred and neglected functions: the crippled arthritic has lost the power of independent action, but he continues to live thanks to the orderly function of the other organs and to the milieu of family or state which supports him. The cardiac patient is prevented from conformity with the social order, but he can use his limbs freely enough to move in a restricted sphere of life. The tuberculosis patient is too weak to participate emotionally in symbiotic existence and must concentrate on his own self. The cancer patient loses control over his self-created world, but he experiences the fate of being subject to the control of others.

These examples of disease as compensation are not oddities, but illustrate a general principle. This principle was not discovered with respect to physical illness, but in psychiatry by Jung (16), who was the first physician to point out the full medical significance of the different psychological types of mankind. These types are distinguished by the overdifferentiation of one function. One-sidedness leads to illness because sooner or later each type encounters a situation which cannot be met realistically by the leading function, but rather requires one of the undifferentiated functions; e.g., feeling might be required from a thinking type. In consequence the neglected function does take over although it is poorly prepared for the task. All this is bearing out the prophecy that "many that are first will be last, and the last first" (Matthew 19:30).

If we view health in its basic meaning as *wholeness* then the way through sickness to death is a way of health. Through the laws of nature we sacrifice those conscious attitudes which have set us apart as individuals. This formulation may appear excessively psychological since it disregards common concepts of physical health and makes the psyche alone significant, whether it be conscious or unconscious. It should be considered, however, that the decay of the body, whether rapid or retarded, is an inherent part of man's participation in life. The statement in the General Confession of the Book of Common Prayer, "There is no health in us," has given expression to this concept that man does not find his fulfillment in his own person.

Religions have at all times and in all places expressed an intuitive insight into the meaning of illness and death. Ritualistic sacrifice seems to be a conscious and deliberate anticipation of the effects of the natural process intended to give death the dignity of

a free human act (3). In this respect it is noteworthy that the
sacrifices of prehistoric and contemporary hunting tribes consist
in the amputation of finger joints "although" hands are particularly important for the hunter, whereas the planters sacrifice human
lives "although" existence on this earth is their main concern (8).

The concept of sacrifice in voluntary or involuntary form is not
a part of modern secular thinking. Man as the conqueror of nature strives for an ideal of total personal health. Illness is therefore conceptualized as damage inflicted by the still unconquered
parts of nature. To accept illness as the expression of an intrinsic
limitation of the personality represents a fundamental denigra-
tion of the image of man. Modern medicine has therefore fla-
grantly sidestepped the insight which was so evident to religious
ages, that man is "(his) own executioner" (John Donne, *Devo-
tion XII*). In the hope of controlling disease, after the example
of scientific victories over inanimate matter, the body is regarded as
a machine which is supposed to function only according to the
laws of physics and chemistry. This automatically excludes personality from consideration. An example of this intellectual blind-
ness is provided by research on cervical cancer. Several investi-
gators have established that this disease is nonexistent among nuns,
but particularly frequent in women who have started sexual activities early in life (25). The attempts at explaining this have
considered physical trauma and virus infection, but have not even
mentioned that there must be a difference between the personalities of girls taking vows of lifelong chastity and those who start an
active and often promiscuous sex life in their teens.

The recognition of disease as an expression of personality gives
the art of healing a wider scope than that provided by physical
theories. The latter theories often deal very effectively with the
physical agents which are involved, but they do not answer the
question why a person became ill in a specific form and at a particular time. Certainly many people recover from illness as a result of physical therapy without gaining any psychological insight.

When we deal with serious conditions, however, such as those described in this introduction, it becomes important to inquire into the way of life which has been involved in the sickness. This inquiry gives the physician an opportunity to help the patient in achieving a healthier way of life instead of merely strengthening him for the continued pursuit of the old one-sided values which led to illness. The attempt to effect such inner change in a patient is certainly more difficult than the treatment of physical symptoms, but its success can mean a great deal for the future. Not only is it important for the physician to understand the patient, when a cure can be effected, but, since every person must die, it is most important that death be understood as a meaningful conclusion to the trial by life. This part of illness has been much neglected in the development of powerful physical methods. Specialists have more and more replaced the family physician who observed the personalities of his patients in their normal environment and who saw it as his task "to watch over the life *and death* of (God's) creatures" (9).

The death of every human being expresses in a unique way the message of the crucifixion. The mortal body and personal initiative are brought to their end on the cross of the superpersonal *law,* the law of biological existence. The vertical beam may be seen as the symbol of the hierarchical order of the world in which the individual is contained, the horizontal beam as a symbol of the symbiotic dependency of man. It has concerned me for many years that the cross is seen so often without the body of the Christ. Is not this the body through which the evolution of all men has passed from generation to generation, transcending forever the law which would endlessly repeat the same patterns of life? It is the dignity of each human being which is expressed by the voice of illness and death, the dignity of having chosen his own way to end. The person may seem insignificant, may be unconscious of any meaning, but he has participated in the physical fate of Christ even as the two thieves did. Contemplating the sick and the dead we learn that there is always a meaning which transcends the law that calls on us to understand and to act with as much purpose as we can. "The Son of God suffered unto the death, not that men might not suffer, but that their suffering might be like His" (19).

Aarne Siirala in the present book has lent his voice to the victims of special forms of man's inhumanity to man. He describes it as psychological illness, in other words, as illness in the sphere in which man is freer than on the biological level of existence. Having seen that even the latter has meaning, the reader may anticipate a message which addresses itself to his immediate concerns and responsibilities.

SELECTED REFERENCES

 1. ABRAMS, R., and FINESINGER, J. E. "Guilt Reactions in Patients with Cancer," *Cancer*, VI (1953), 474.
 2. BOOTH, GOTTHARD. "Organ Function and Form Perception," *Psychosomatic Medicine*, VIII (1946), 367.
 3. ———— "Variety in Personality and Its Relation to Health," *Review of Religion*, X (1946), 385.
 4. ———— "Health from the Standpoint of the Physician," in PAUL B. MAVES (ed.), *The Church and Mental Health*. New York: Scribner, 1953.
 5. ———— "The Psychological Examination of Candidates for the Ministry," in HANS HOFMANN (ed.), *The Ministry and Mental Health*. New York: Association, 1960.
 6. ———— "Values in Nature and in Psychotherapy," *Archives of General Psychiatry*, VIII (1963), 22.
 7. ———— "Cancer and Humanism," in *Third International Conference on Psychosomatic Aspects of Neoplastic Disease*. London: Pitman, 1964.
 8. CAMPBELL, JOSEPH. *The Masks of God*. New York: Viking, 1959.
 9. COHEN, A. E. "The Daily Prayer of a Clergyman-Physician," *Journal of Religion and Health*, I (1961), 64.
10. DE LAMETTRIE, J. O. *L'Homme machine*. Leyden, 1750. Quoted from *Encyclopaedia Britannica* (1963), XIII, 620a.
11. ENGEL, G. "Selection of Clinical Material in Psychosomatic Medicine," *Psychosomatic Medicine*, XVI (1954), 368.
12. FREUD, SIGMUND. *Beyond the Pleasure Principle*. New York: Liveright, 1922, and Bantam, 1959.
13. ———— "Analysis Terminable and Interminable," *Collected Papers*, Vol. V. London: Hogarth, 1950.

14. HARLOW, H. F. "Development of Affection in Primates," in E. L. BLISS (ed.), *Roots of Behavior.* New York: Hoeber, 1962.
15. ———. *Nature and Development of the Affectional Systems.* ("Salmon Lectures.") New York: Academy of Medicine, 1960.
16. JUNG, C. G. "Psychological Types," *Collected Works,* Vol. VI. New York: Pantheon, 1958.
17. KIERKEGAARD, SOREN. "Sickness unto Death," in R. BRETALL (ed.), *A Kierkegaard Anthology.* Princeton: Princeton Univ., 1946.
18. LeSHAN, L. "Psychological States as Factors in the Development of Malignant Disease: A Critical Review," *Journal of the National Cancer Institute,* XXII (1958), 1.
19. MACDONALD, G. *Quoted in* C. S. LEWIS, *The Problem of Pain.* New York: Macmillan, 1944.
20. NAUTS, H. C., FOWLER, G. A. and BOGATKO, F. H. *A Review of the Influence of Bacterial Infection and Bacterial Products in Man.* Stockholm: Acta Med. Scand., 1953.
21. PORTMANN, A. *Biologie und Geist.* Zurich: Rhein Verlag, 1956.
22. QUISENBERRY, W. B. "Sociological Factors in Cancer in Hawaii," in VERA RUBIN et al., *Culture, Society and Health.* ("Annals," LXXXIV, 795.) New York: Academy of Sciences, 1961.
23. RICHTER, C. P. "The Phenomenon of Sudden Unexplained Death in Animals and Men," in HERMAN FEIFEL (ed.), *The Meaning of Death.* New York: McGraw-Hill, 1959.
24. ROTHSCHILD, F. S. "Laws of Symbolic Mediation in the Dynamics of Self and Personality," *Annals of the New York Academy of Science* XCVI (1962), 774-84.
25. ROTKIN, I. D. "Relation of Adolescent Coitus to Cervical Cancer Risk," *Journal of the American Medical Association,* CLXXIX (1962), 486.
26. SPITZ, RENÉ A. "Hospitalism," in RUTH S. EISSLER et al. (eds.), *Psychoanalytic Study of the Child,* Vol. I. New York: Int. Univs., 1945.
27. ———. *No and Yes: On the Genesis of Human Communication.* New York: Int. Univs., 1957.
28. SZONDI, L. *Schicksalanalyse,* Basel: Benno Schwabe, 1944.
29. SZONDI, L.; MOSER, V.; and WEBB, M. *The Szondi Test.* Philadelphia: Lippincott, 1959.
30. TINBERGEN, NIKALAAS. *The Study of Instinct.* New York: Oxford, 1955.
31. UEXKÜLL, J. VON. *Theoretical Biology.* New York: Abingdon, 1931.
32. WARBURG, O. *Über den Stoffwechsel der Tumoren.* Berlin: Springer, 1926.
33. WITTKOWER, E. *A Psychiatrist Looks at Tuberculosis.* London: N.A.P.T., 1949.

Chapter 1

The Reality of Illness and the
Ambiguity of Words

1. Our Illness

During the final days of the Second World War, armed forces
arrived to liberate those who had survived the gas chambers of a
concentration camp located in the heart of Western Christendom.
With the army came a group of physicians who, after giving emer-
gency treatment and arranging hospitalization for those who were
in the worst condition, had the job of classifying the other survivors into several groups. They prepared questionnaires and then
lined up the survivors to begin their work. As one of the physicians was examining the former prisoners' muscles to determine
their capacity for physical work, he suddenly stopped in front of
one of the victims. He felt that he read in her despairing eyes the
thought: "The concentration camp continues. You are doing just
what they did."

The doctor sought permission from his superiors to work out
an alternative procedure. When permission had been granted, a
group of other doctors and several hundred of the victims volun-
teered to work with this doctor. They abandoned the questionnaires and the line-ups and began rather to study the meaning of
the whole situation.

Gradually an image of the situation in which they were living
came into focus. The concentration camp had not come into being
accidentally. It was man's work. Men had prepared it for men.

Thoughts in the minds of men had taken form in the camp which they now knew in all its horror; through the concentration camp men had tried to solve some of the conflicts of their own society. The structure of the camp made explicit the inner conflicts of the society in which it was born.

The group began to study the structure of the camp as one performs a biopsy of tissue from a sick organism. They asked one another: How is it possible that this tissue is from the same organism which yields such different forms of life? How can these concentration camps belong to the same landscape as churches, universities, schools, hospitals, and homes? What does this tissue tell about the organism from which it comes? These questions they could not answer. Each question evoked new questions.

Gradually the group began to study its own part in the birth of the concentration camps. The tissue began to speak to them of the character of their own life as a group. As they studied the origin of the camp and its present structure, they were forced to ask themselves, "Would we have been any different from the men whose opinions or indifference created the camp?"

From this questioning came the decision to remain together and to attempt to learn from the experiences of the concentration camp. They decided to build a camp where the hidden attitudes that had led to the original camp could be revealed, and where they could seek the means of healing this sickness. In the concentration camp were concentrated the sickest and most crooked processes in the organism of the society. Would it not be possible, they asked, to create a camp where the opposite processes were concentrated? Why is there among us only a concentration of destructive powers? Would it not be possible to create a concentration camp of healing powers?

Out of the dreary shadows of death they began to seek fountains of life. When they found a place for their camp in France they called it *l'Eau Vive*, The Living Water. Into this camp of life they sought to build the opposite of the death camp even in the smallest details. In making decisions they studied how and why the equivalent decision had been made in the death camp. From these studies there developed a form for the community life of the camp of The Living Water. The death camp had been closed and therefore the camp of life had to be open. The victims in the death camp had been carefully screened and therefore everyone was welcome at the camp of life. In the camp of death there was no freedom of movement, at the camp of life people could come and go at will. During ten years, for periods of weeks or months, to the camp of The Living Water there came thousands of people who, listening together to the voice of illness, tried to find ways of healing.

When the core group of *l'Eau Vive* decided to break camp, and those who had participated went their many ways to continue the search individually, it was resolved that nothing should be written about their camp. The death camps had become worlds of "red tape" and "objective research" which denied all participation. A perverted use of words had made real human encounter impossible. Words became mere signs and were used as a means of excluding such groups as were not tolerated by those who determined the meaning of words. In the death camps the written, fixed word was used as a substitute for the living, spoken word. Studies in these perversions of words alerted the people of *l'Eau Vive* to the difference between the letter that kills and the spirit that gives life.

In the camp of The Living Water the living, spoken word was used openly and publicly to express the common experience. Words were to be tested by listening to the voice of their previous perversion, yet the tragic end of *l'Eau Vive* itself—it was dissolved by the destructive action of one of its leaders who attempted to get all authority into his hands—speaks with eloquence of the ambiguity of the reality in which all healing takes place.[1]

2. The Problem

This story opens for us the problem which we shall be consider-
ing in the pages that follow. Briefly stated, the issue is this: serious questions which demand answers have been raised by the encounter with the illnesses of individuals and communities in
Western Christianity. This encounter calls into question essential
marks of Christianity: the proclamation of the word and the establishment of community.

Research always begins with a problem.[2] A problem arises
whenever experience fails to fit an existing idea, or when events
call prevailing attitudes into question. When one does not have
the facts necessary to explain a situation, or is unable even to construct an adequate hypothesis, he is faced with a problem.

Not all research, however, deals with the clarifying of problem
situations. In some stages of research the task is to test the logical consequences of a theory, using the methods of formal logic.
If the issue is that of verifying a theory, one has to proceed mainly
by empirical methods, the character of the problem defining the
methods to be used in every instance.

The initial stage of all research, though, is the clarifying of the
problem. Now before we can come directly to the problem to
which we are here addressing ourselves, it is necessary to examine
more closely the character of this clarifying.

The studies of Galileo provide the most relevant example.[3]
Galileo and his contemporaries suspected that Aristotelian physics
was self-contradictory. The problem arose when Galileo observed
that the motion of a projectile did not follow Aristotle's theories.
Faced with this phenomenon he had several alternatives. He might
simply have continued to collect more material by measuring the
motions of different projectiles, deriving from such research certain general conclusions. Or he might have questioned the theories themselves, basing his conclusions on other established facts.
If, however, Galileo had followed either of these paths, it is prob-

able that he would not have come to the conclusions which led to radically new developments in science. It is also very improbable that he would have found solutions simply by use of the imagination. The imagination alone seldom has the power to free itself of traditional theories and solutions.

Galileo followed none of these methods, but instead concentrated on an analysis of the problem itself. He began to analyze the structure of the problem which had arisen out of his observations of the motion of the projectile. It soon became obvious to him that the core of the problem was not the projectile, but rather the Aristotelian definition of the nature of force. Galileo was not content simply to study the motion of the projectile; he concentrated on an analysis of force itself. This analysis enabled him to make observations of phenomena which the existing theories had obscured. His analysis of the different factors in the problem led him to put the questions in new ways. He then began to test whether these new questions were appropriate for solving the problem itself.

For our purposes, the important point is that in the first stage of any research one has to pay strict attention to the structure of the situation to be studied. Methods of research are not predetermined; they are dictated by the nature of the problem with which one is dealing. Before we can even form a hypothesis we must analyze the problem, and this analysis will lead us to the phenomena out of which a hypothesis then can be formed—and subsequent research pursued.[4]

The problem which is the subject of this book is multifaceted. The phenomena which give rise to the questions we shall pose are certain experiences in the encounter with illness. The central factor in the problem, however, is the reality of illness itself, something which our everyday experience of illness shows to be most difficult to understand. Illness is like an unhewn stone which cuts the hands of anyone who tries to work with it. While many elements in our existence fit easily into place, illness seems always to be a stumbling block.[5] There is in the encounter with illness something which shatters the interpretation of life we have previously formed. In studying the architecture of illness, one cannot use methods which are appropriate only to structures not involving illness. The multidimensional nature of the thing itself puts the study of illness in a special category. The history of therapy, as we later will try to show, demonstrates this clearly. The reality of illness is so complex that it repeatedly frustrates and disrupts the studies aimed at analyzing it, until no single vantage point suffices from which to view the whole matter.

The history of the encounter with illness demonstrates that illness must be studied from many angles,[6] and yet in the experience and discussion of recent decades—which we shall attempt to analyze in the final section of Chapter 2—no new theory of the character of illness has arisen. The theory based on natural science, which dominated for centuries in Western culture, has been shown to be inadequate. A new alternative theory is still in the process of being developed.[7]

The encounter with illness with which this book began has already indicated the theme which will be central in our general discussion. The story of *l'Eau Vive* points to illness as a reality which extends to the whole organism—both the individual organism and the community organism—and illness is seen as reaching to the most vital functions, even to the formation of the words of human existence. This theme of the all-inclusive character of the reality of illness touches the very heart of the Christian life, that is, the formation of communities (parishes, denominations) and the proclamation of the word (preaching, teaching).

Christian communities—regardless of their particular interpretation of the nature of the church—are concerned with the ministry of the word, the word that destroys and the word that saves both individuals and communities. It is the task of all Christian communities to discuss the criteria to be used in differentiating the "right" from the "wrong" words, and to discuss the place of the proclamation of the word in the total life of the community organism.

We would underscore the fact that the "word" is of crucial importance in the sickness and health of an organism. In the encounter with illness a distinction must be made between a sick and a healthy forming of words. Participants in the encounter have tried to analyze how becoming sick and becoming well are manifest in this matter of the forming of words. The study of the forming of words and thoughts from the point of view of pathology[8] is a sign of a deep process, the wellsprings of which are to be located in the very depths of our Western culture.[9] With the end of the last century the whirlpools of these springs began, however, to gain such strength that one can really begin to speak of a crisis in the encounter with illness. The tendencies within this crisis which emphasize the significance of the word in the process of becoming sick and well are manifest in those developments which are called psychological, psychiatric, psychoanalytical, psychotherapeutic, and psychosomatic.[10]

In view of the variety both of these terms and of the vocabulary used by different schools of thought, it is appropriate at this point that we take time to analyze the principles which we are to use. This variety—and often confusion—in the use of words in research dealing with the encounter with illness is not an accidental phenomenon. In the encounter with illness a conscious attempt is made to find healing for the perversion of words. It is natural then that the healing word must in some measure share the illness of the perverted word. The forming of words both in the actual encounter with illness and in the examination of the nature of illness must conform itself to the reality of which the words speak. When the encounter with illness is based on a fixed conceptual system this forming of words will be something quite different. In any fixed conceptual system the classifications used are inade-

quate to deal with the whole reality involved and thus "break
down." This becomes apparent, for example, in discussions concerning the character of diagnosis among those whose encounter
with illness is the special object of this investigation.[11] Calling the
illness by name is considered to be an important part of the encounter itself. The diagnosis is already part of the therapy. Thus
we can see that terminological questions are a factor in the problem with which we are to deal.

3.   Human Existence in the Light of Illness

In the encounter with illness special attention must be paid to
the symbolic character of words.[12] This emphasis is not, however,
characteristic merely of the encounter with illness.[13] Discussion of
symbols and of the symbolic character of words is a symptom of a
process in our culture which is both caused by the encounter with
illness and mirrored in it.[14]

The inability of certain thought categories to express the reality
of illness inevitably leads to an analysis of the symbolic character
of words.[15] In the present confrontation between the sick and the
potential healers, the thought patterns in which illness has been
traditionally understood have been radically called into question.
This is expressed differently in different phases of the encounter
with illness, yet common to all such encounter is a questioning of
that way of thinking which regards a relationship to men and a
relationship to things in the same light. Such an approach gives
the same value to men themselves as to the objects men may have
under consideration. The subject, the observer, abstracts himself,
maintaining a clear dichotomy between subject and object, imagin-
ing that he can thus obtain an adequate understanding of human
experience.[16] In the encounter with illness, however, a protest
against this procedure has arisen. Man cannot be studied in the
categories of non-human existence. The basic character of human

existence is not that of an inquiring subject in a world of objective realities; man's genuine existence does not depend upon his ability to do such an inquiring in an adequate way.[17] In the light of experiences with the sickness and health of the human organism, the structure of human existence has now become an object of study from a new point of view.

When the structure of human existence is seen from the perspective opened by illness, those theories according to which the world of consciousness is the most decisive factor in integrating man and reality are called into question. The total structure of our life situation—whether or not we are conscious of it—is more decisive than the images which we have formed of it. Reality cannot be identified with consciousness. The structure of man's existence is not determined by what he decides. Viewed in the light of illness man appears as a being who is not the captain of his own ship. It is the actual structure of life itself, which man experiences symbolically, not his conscious comprehension of it, that determines man's path. When man is studied in the light of his illness it becomes clear that the basic structure of human existence is that which has often been called primitive:

> Throughout all cultures the same phenomenon can be observed: they exist by means of an all-pervading structure which regulates the individual lives of its members. The authority of this structure decides which human qualities and functions are favored, which restricted, which tolerated. . . Since the mechanistic scientist considers goal directed activities the basic concern of man, all cultural structures appear to him as irrational authorities. They do interfere with many pursuits of which human beings are inherently capable, and which some of them consciously desire. Evidently a rationalistic culture, constructed to satisfy the wishes of individuals, would have to eliminate everything not related to those wishes often considered the expression of "basic human nature." The primitive accepts cultural interference with his needs and wishes, because the symbolic organization of life protects him. . . He knows intuitively that the forces of the unconscious are stronger than the power of the conscious mind

and that, therefore, conscious life should be kept in harmony with the order of the unconscious. Symbolic practices are the means by which conscious life can be directed along safe channels.[18]

From this perspective of man's illness and healing it becomes clear that man's life in the world of symbols is of essential importance.

In an encounter with reality which maintains a dichotomy between subject and object, the dominating categories classify man as an instinctive being who perceives and forms concepts through his senses. The study of the formation of words which is based on this dichotomy concentrates on an analysis of the function of the senses.[19] The healthy forming of words is then considered to be dependent upon healthy senses. The senses which function healthfully mediate correct perceptions, and organize them with the help of memory and associations into a conceptual system which is realistic. The words are then means and signs of man's satisfying his needs—means and signs through which he is in contact with his environment. Perversions in the forming of words are symptoms of disturbances in the functions of the senses. The degree of humanity then depends primarily upon man's ability to make observations of reality—both in himself and in his environment—and upon his power to direct his life in accordance with observations and perceptions which are tested in his own and in common experiences: a healthy soul in the healthy body (*mens sana in corpore sano*).

In the deepening understanding of human existence which results from the encounter with illness, there emerges a picture of man which shatters the conclusions of those who maintain a dichotomy between subject and object. Increasingly, man is seen to live in a relationship to his fellow beings and to his environment that is totally different from what was heretofore supposed by the psychology based only on natural science.[20] Fundamental questions are now being asked in a new way. When in this study we call the basic function of the human organism a "symbolic" function we are attempting to disengage ourselves from the old categories and from the old way of asking the basic questions.

We are seeking a new point of view for the understanding of man—a point of view which maintains an organic unity between man's physical character and the psychological content of his behavior. The person in the physical organism is encountered in the meanings and contents of his words and deeds, his habits and gestures; this meaning and content is encountered as an expression of the physical organism of the person. Even if the being of man cannot be identified with the physical structure of existence—as the meaning of a sentence is not identified with the vowels and consonants of a sentence—yet the physical organism and the person living in it form an organic unity in which the person symbolizes the organism and the organism the person.[21]

The experience of Helen Keller has often been presented as a concrete example of what is meant by the symbolic character of the forming of words.[22] A blind deaf-mute, she has learned to use language in a richer way than many persons whose senses are acute in perceiving reality. Here we have a telling illustration of the fact that the world of man is structured by language. The word is at the very center of human nature, and the forming of words is a most basic function of the human organism.[23] The word is not only a means by which man expresses his perceptions and experiences; it is an organic part of man.[24] The human organism is verbal, and its basic tendency is the effort to symbolize. Helen Keller tells in her autobiography how the reality of language and word dawned upon her, and how the word opened up experience for her. She tells how her teacher, about to take a walk, brought her a hat which was for her a sign of going out. "This thought, if a wordless sensation may be called a thought, made me hop and skip with pleasure." She then goes on to describe the situation in which her hand was placed—in water from the well:

As the cool stream gushed over my hand my teacher spelled into the other the word water, first slowly, then rapidly. I stood still, my whole attention fixed upon the motion of her fingers. Suddenly I felt a misty consciousness as of something forgotten— a thrill of returning thought; and somehow the mystery of language was revealed to me. I knew then that w-a-t-e-r meant the wonderful cool something that was flowing over my hand. The living word awakened my soul, gave it light, hope, joy, set it free. . . . I left the well-house eager to learn. Everything had a name, and each name gave birth to a new thought. As we returned to the house every object which I touched seemed to quiver with life.[25]

When the experience of Miss Keller is analyzed as an example of the symbolic character of the forming of words, attention must be especially directed to that distinction which she makes between nonverbal and verbal sensation. When she experiences sensations as mere signs which point to something to be expected, her world of experience is still very limited. The realization that the word participates in part in that reality which it names opens for her a new world. The word as sign, as signal, has a different function from the word as symbol.[26] The word as symbol is a part of that reality which it expresses and creates a different kind of contact from the word as signal.[27] Even animals understand the language of signals; only man experiences the word as symbol.

4. Symbolic and Diabolic Forming of Words

Our analysis of the symbolic function of words is an attempt to ascertain what kind of word formation makes an organism human. In the encounter with illness, the function of the word is of central importance as the organism becomes sick and well again. In therapy and in the study of the forming of words one has to see beyond the language of signals to an essentially human use of words.[28] One central purpose in the encounter with illness is to listen to the forming of words in therapy and in the study of therapy in such a way that man really encounters man.[29] The words which we use to express the content of the encounter with illness serve not only to describe the illness, but also to convey the message of disease to others. The words have this symbolic function both in therapy and in the study of therapy. The attempt is made to use words so that they create both wholeness and unity in the man who has gone to pieces, and genuine human community (relationship) beyond the simple "sign-signal" contact. In ancient Greek the word symbol meant, among other things, that which re-establishes community between realities which belong together but have become separated. When a guest from afar was leaving, the host broke some object and gave half to the departing guest. When the guest returned, perhaps years later, he was accepted in the home where his half fitted together with the half that had been left behind. The object whose pieces could thus be fitted together was called a symbol.[30]

When in the following we speak of the "symbolic" function of words, we mean the unifying function of words as they create organic unity in the human organism. The "diabolical" words are those which dissolve the unity and wholeness. When the symbolic function of a word is perverted, the word becomes diabolic.

At least three degrees of unity between the human organism and its human and nonhuman environment can be distinguished. That unity which is marked by nonverbal sensations we call *contact*.[31] Contact is realized through stimuli and through the response caused by them. That unity which is based on "sign language" where the words are used as signals, we call *communication*.[32] The presupposition of the verbal exchange between men is a common understanding of the meaning of words. Communication is based on contact, but it is qualitatively different in character from contact. Contact is nonverbal; communication is verbal. The human organism is not, however, only in contact and in communication with reality. Out of his experience man forms symbols through which he lives in a special kind of unity with his human and nonhuman environment. This unity—which includes also con-

tact and communication—we call *communion,* symbolic or sacramental communion.[33] The character of human life lived together
as communion is one of the central emphases in the encounter with
illness which is the subject of this study.

5. The Therapeutic Encounter with Illness

The terminology used in the encounter with illness forms an
essential element in the problem we have been trying to analyze.
This is evident in the very names frequently given to the various
movements in the encounter with illness: psychological, psychiatric, psychoanalytic, psychotherapeutic, and psychosomatic.[34] Behind all these expressions is the Greek root word *psyche.* Different schools of thought have tried in their own circles to agree upon
the meaning of the word *psyche* in order to make communication
possible. Yet whenever we try to listen to and interpret the communication of a particular school of thought from outside the confines of the language of that school, the terminological ambiguity
becomes apparent. We are required always to determine which
reality the word *psyche* is symbolizing at a given moment. Since
in this study we are not working from within the framework of
a particular school of thought, it is not meaningful to make a
choice between the different definitions of *psyche.* Rather, our
attempt is to listen to and interpret the different expressions used
by the various schools as symbols which convey the meaning of the
reality of illness. The Greek word *psyche* expressed originally the
notion that something or someone lives.[35] The word psychological
will be used here in the sense of this root meaning, to speak of the
organisms as living unities. When we speak of an organism as a
psychological reality, we mean simply the organism as it lives in
the totality of reality (i.e., the interplay of the powers of reality).[36]
Our intention is to listen to the voice of illness as it is interpreted by the therapeutic schools of thought which encounter and
examine illness as a psychological reality. Our main concern will

be to sketch the message of illness itself and not to analyze the varying outlooks of the particular schools which convey that message. Instead of calling the schools which interpret the voice of illness by the names which they have given themselves (Freudian, Adlerian, Jungian, Neo-Freudian, etc.), we will generally use the common terms therapy and therapeutic. Only when the context requires it will a particular school be singled out. The terms therapy and therapeutic will mean, therefore, an encounter with illness in which the illness is cared for and studied as a psychological reality.[37] The Greek words *therapeia and therapeuō* originally meant "service" or "serving," where the serving person was in such a personal relationship to the person served that he not only cared for him but also shared his burden. Gradually these words came to mean the medical care of the sick, the physician's healing.[38]

6. The Prophetic Situation in a Sick Reality

We have been driven to these studies by the dilemma which the therapeutic encounter with illness and study of illness has created for "Christian theology" in Western culture. The dilemma will be analyzed with reference to the proclamation of the word and the formation of community. While the analysis is primarily from within the Protestant and particularly the Lutheran tradition, the word theology in this discussion embraces the whole history of Christian preaching and community life. The "Protestant" perspective actually developed in the context of a discussion generated by Roman Catholic Christianity. Since Protestantism is an element in Western Catholic tradition, analysis of its expressions leads necessarily to a consideration of the whole of Western Christianity.[39]

By the same token, "Roman Catholicism" is a word in a discussion which it has not itself created. The various traditions in Christianity all derive their roots from those events to which the biblical literature bears witness. Accordingly, all theological research in Christianity is basically a discussion of the character of those same events. On the one hand, the discussions of the content and structure of preaching and community life in different Christian traditions lead to an analysis of the biblical literature; on the other hand, all studies of the Bible and its events mean participating in the discussion of a particular Christian tradition. When one form of church (be it Lutheran, Anglican, Baptist, or Roman Catholic) proclaims itself the only real Christian church, or its point of view the only biblical one, it excludes itself from that discussion where the very foundations of Christian preaching and community are being considered. This kind of ecclesiasticism and biblicism does not recognize the existence of the problems mentioned above; dialogue with the therapeutic encounter with illness is regarded as unnecessary for theology in its analysis of the essentials, namely, the proclamation of the word and the formation of community. Such a church is then structurally similar to those scientific schools of thought which regard as definitive and final the particular expressions which they use. In discussion between such churches a conventionalized form of interaction replaces all existential communication and communal unity. Then mutual interaction can take place only on the condition that the established sign language is followed.

The way our problem is stated presupposes that a continuous discussion of the fundamentals of the proclamation of the word and of the formation of community is altogether necessary. This necessity derives from the inner pressure of Christian preaching and community life. Our choice of the word prophecy for use in association with the word therapy was deliberate. The world of Christian proclamation and formation of community, for which the therapeutic encounter with illness has created a dilemma, is in its basic structure a "prophetic" reality. It had its origin in and is nurtured by a living, creating word. Christian preaching and formation of community aim at integrating individuals and communities in a prophetic situation. The proclamation of the word and the formation of community burgeon out of the midst of real events, the content and structure of which have been conveyed to us by the biblical writings. These events force us to live in a situation where the most decisive factor in individual and community life becomes the symbolic forming of words.[40] The words become either "symbolic," creating communion, or "diabolic," destroying both individual and communal unity. A living word which fulfills its symbolic function quickens man; a dead, diabolic word destroys man. The way individuals and communities watch over the words which determine their life is of basic and vital importance, for human life is built on the word. Man is differentiated from the rest of creation primarily by the fact that in the center of human existence is the word. Man is a being whose life is a continuous confrontation between the symbolic use of the word which creates the wholeness of life and the diabolic use of the word which destroys the unity of life. To put it differently, we have been placed in a prophetic situation where we must in our conscience draw a line between right and wrong prophecy.[41]

When we use the terms prophecy and prophetic our reference will again be to the original meaning of the word in Greek. The word *prophētēs* appeared in Greek as early as the fifth century B.C. It was used in connection with verbs which meant "saying," "speaking," "public proclamation," "explaining." It was used, among other times, when a common decision of the legislature of the people was proclaimed.[42] By thus referring to the origin of the word we would emphasize that the prophetic function belongs to human existence as such. It is in the very nature of man's being to form words through which the individual and the community express publicly a certain interpretation, a certain "prophecy" of their experience.[43] In human experience words either grow into symbols creating unity or are diabolically perverted into destroying unity. Individuals and communities decide on different grounds what they consider to be constructive "proclaiming of the word"[44] and what destructive, what is a therapeutic use of words and what

is not.[45] They all make the distinction, however, and try to discover the difference between "right" and "wrong" prophecy.

Within society there is a tendency for different prophecies ema-
nating from various individuals and groups—ideological, scientific, or religious—to seek to control the forming of words.[46] Each
tries to dictate the words of society. Despite this common temptation, we will in our examination of a theological interpretation of
the prophetic situation—the problem of the Christian proclamation
of the word and formation of community—seek to avoid being
dogmatic. No particular individual or community can validly
claim to represent the "right" prophecy merely by appealing to
the original sources of Christianity or to some form of Christian
community.[47] All Christian proclamation of the word, whether the
word of faith which is sharpened through the conscience of the
individual Christian or the common prophetic word which is tested
in the crucible of the Christian community, is under the same general limitations as all human forming of words. The word proclaimed as the word of God has been shaped in the forge of human reality and thus participates in the discussion between different prophecies concerning constructive and destructive words.
Christian proclamation of the word, when it remains true to its
foundations, does not shut off discussion between the different
prophecies. On the contrary, it fosters that discussion.[48] While
particular prophecies fortify the positions they have chosen for
themselves, the Christian proclamation of the word and the formation of community challenges the individual and the community
to live in a prophetic situation where the living word is ever
sought, and where an attempt is ever made to articulate the word
which breaks away from and overcomes the perverted word.[49]

If Christian proclamation of the word and formation of community is thought of in this way, the study of Christian theology
becomes something quite different from what it would be on the
presupposition that Christian preaching and formation of community became fixed at some definite period in history. In the

latter case, the material of theological study is primarily the tradition of "right" prophecy. If, on the other hand, theology acknowledges its participation in the prophetic situation, and recognizes that the words which it forms are not exclusively its own creation but issue from the union of theology with all other words of prophecy, then every effort to find criteria for differentiating right and wrong prophecy can properly be said to be "theological" study.

When the term "Christian theology" was used in the opening paragraph of this section, it was intentionally enclosed in quotation marks. It is not possible to define at the outset what kind of study is ultimately and authentically "Christian," because all theology grows in a prophetic situation, and—like every kind of prophecy—is subject to testing.[50] The use of theological words is as open to perversion as the use of any other words. The history of theology, as we intend to show, contains many examples of "diabolic" vocabulary, a vocabulary which destroys the unity of life. By "Christian theology" we mean a study which has been made and is continually being made in the framework of a community which understands itself to be within the history of the Christian church. So great is the challenge which has come from those studies outside Christian theology which attempt to determine proper criteria for distinguishing between healing and destructive words, between right and wrong prophecy, that one must ask to what extent theology has really fulfilled the prophetic function of Christianity. From this point of view, expressions of the therapeutic encounter with illness which aim to analyze the criteria for differentiating between the healing and the destroying word have to be regarded as theological expressions. The character or focus of theological study is determined not by any constellation of established positions in a certain historical situation but exclusively by the structure of the situation as it has been shaped by those events which form the foundation of the Christian proclamation of the word and formation of community. If the therapeutic encounter with illness and study of illness, of which we have been speaking, is to-day outside the limits of what is now called "theology," this does not mean that its voice should not be heard in the theological analysis of the present prophetic situation.

Chapter 2

The Encounter with Illness
in the Light of Its History

1. The Voice of Illness in the Origins of Christian Prophecy

Whenever a deep crisis occurs in a culture, the study of history must begin from a new viewpoint. When the starting points which have been relied upon in the writing of history break down, then history must be seen in a new light.

The therapeutic encounter with illness has caused a deep crisis in our Western culture. The experience of illness as a meaningful psychological reality has opened a new perspective from which can be studied not only the history of medical care and medical science, but also the history of other elements in our culture. A new vista is opened before our eyes; we can now see reality in terms strikingly different from the ones in which our school history books have tutored us. The study of the history of the encounter with illness from the therapeutic point of view thus calls into question many of the conclusions of traditional church history. The customary inquiry concerning Christian life and theology is now subject to a new interplay of forces; church history is thrown into a new light.

This is not surprising. If there has occurred in Western Christianity a real separation between prophecy and therapy, it is to be expected that as we examine the new interrelation between the two, we shall also be required to ask the reasons for the separation. The new interrelation has led to a study of the origin of the history of Christianity from a new perspective, and it can now be seen that in these origins the prophetic and the therapeutic function of the community are organically integrated. It has gradually become clear that the contemporary therapeutic encounter with illness draws from springs which are the sources of Christianity.[1]

A systematic study of the mutual interrelationship between prophetic proclamation and the therapeutic encounter with illness as it appears in biblical writings is outside our present focus.[2] In the following we shall refer only to such biblical material[3] as has already been brought into the center of discussions concerning the encounter with illness.

In the mutual relationship between prophecy and therapy a central issue has consistently been the question of the character of the proclamation of the Old Testament prophets. There is one emphasis of special importance: in the prophetic visions described in the Old Testament the universe is viewed as sick, as a reality which needs healing. The coming salvatory events which the prophets proclaim mean the healing of the whole universe.[4] Illness is viewed as cosmic, as something which extends throughout the whole universe.[5] Various elements of nature are in conflict with one another. Between man and nature there exists a mutual hostility, and the covenant of God with the beasts of the field and the birds of the air (Hos. 2:18) is broken. The earth has become sick and brings forth thorns and thistles (Gen. 3:18). There is a controversy between men and animals. The life of man is full of pain and affliction, and mutual relationships between men are broken (3:4-8). The illness also appears in social perversion:

> The patriarchal power of man over woman, the division of languages, the cleavage between nomadic and agricultural forms of existence, the rise of world powers and tyrants . . . all this is the state of society which needs a healer. . . . And social evils, especially idolatrous tyrants, false prophets and messiahs, pagan empires and religions, are the work of demons. . . . Nature, society and soul are subject to the same principle of disintegration.[6]

Like the illness itself, the healing is seen as cosmic.[7] In the coming messianic time the entire sick creation will be healed. "The wolf shall dwell with the lamb, and the leopard shall lie down with the kid, and the calf and the lion and the fatling together, and a little child shall lead them . . . . The sucking child shall play over the hole of the asp, and the weaned child shall put his hand on the adder's den. They shall not hurt or destroy in all my holy mountain; . . . The jealousy . . . shall depart, and those who harass . . . shall be cut off" (Isa. 11:6, 8-9, 13).

It is powerfully clear in the prophetic writings of the Old Testament that the messianic healing reaches to the deepest turbulence of the common and universal sickness. Mankind, in the grasp of illness, encounters healing from within the illness. It is within the solidarity of illness that common and universal healing is experienced. The Messiah who appears in order to be the healer of all acts in the midst of the most painful depths of that illness which holds all in its grasp. "Behold, my servant shall prosper, he shall be exalted and lifted up, and shall be very high. As many were astonished at him—his appearance was so marred, beyond human semblance, and his form beyond that of the sons of men— so shall he startle many nations" (52:13-15). "For he grew up before him like a young plant, and like a root out of dry ground; he had no form or comeliness that we should look at him, and no beauty that we should desire him. He was despised and rejected by men; a man of sorrows, and acquainted with grief; and as one from whom men hide their faces he was despised, and we esteemed him not. Surely he has borne our griefs and carried our sorrows; yet we esteemed him stricken, smitten by God, and afflicted. But he was wounded for our transgressions, he was bruised for our iniquities; upon him was the chastisement that made us whole, and with his stripes we are healed" (53:2-5).

These scattered references to Old Testament prophecy show that the emphases on the commonness and universality of illness and on the importance of listening to the message hidden in illness touch themes which are found in the wellsprings of Christian prophecy. These passages lead us, therefore, to ask how the prophetic function is influenced by the acceptance and rejection of the notion of the universality of illness. We are compelled, furthermore, to examine what the prophetic proclamation of salvation from sin means as we seek to listen to the message of illness.

When the writings of the New Testament witness to the faith that Jesus is the Christ, the Messiah promised by Old Testament prophecy, the prophetic and the therapeutic functions are united in an organic and inseparable way. "When John heard in prison about the deeds of the Christ, he sent word by his disciples and said to him, 'Are you he who is to come, or shall we look for another?' And Jesus answered them, 'Go and tell John what you hear and see: the blind receive their sight and the lame walk, lepers are cleansed and the deaf hear, and the dead are raised up, and the poor have good news preached to them'" (Matt. 11:2-5). "And preach as you go, saying, 'The kingdom of Heaven is at hand.' Heal the sick, raise the dead, cleanse lepers, cast out demons. You received without pay, give without pay" (10:7-8). "He called the twelve together and gave them power and authority over all demons and to cure diseases, and he sent them out to preach the kingdom of God and to heal" (Luke 9:1-2). "When they heard it, they lifted their voices together to God and said, 'Sovereign Lord, who didst make the heaven and the earth and the sea and everything in them, . . . And now, Lord, look upon their threats, and grant to thy servants to speak thy word with all boldness, while thou stretchest out thy hand to heal, and signs and wonders are performed through the name of thy holy servant Jesus" (Acts 4:24, 29-30).

These and similar passages from the New Testament have come into focus when questions of sickness and health have been analyzed in Christian theology and different interpretations of their meaning have been presented.[8] The texts, nevertheless, speak so clearly of the fact that salvation and the healing of illness belong together, that there can consequently be no establishment of community based on the biblical writings which does not face the question of the interdependence of prophecy and therapy.[9] It is possible to have different opinions and interpretations, but it is not possible to avoid the question of the mutual interrelation of prophecy and therapy.[10]

2. The Voice of Illness Is Stifled

Within the context of the present therapeutic encounter with illness there is a growing awareness of the voice of illness, and the response of previous ages to this voice can be viewed in a new light. This present awareness is marked on the one hand by a recognition of the commonness and universality of illness, and on the other hand by an integration of illness and therapy with the dramatic conflict of those powers which save and destroy life. In previous periods of history different cultural and ecclesiastical attitudes have resulted in quite different conclusions. A study of the treatment of the mentally ill throws into very clear outline the attitude of earlier communities and individuals toward illness.[11]

Biblical writings speak in powerful language of the importance of mental illness to the whole people. They speak of the power of salvation against illness;[12] and the conquest of the powers which cause mental illness is seen as a sign of the messianic age.[13]

By contrast, church history tells of the isolation and persecution of the mentally ill. The history of the reaction of the community to the mentally ill is the history of the oppression of the mentally ill in Western Christianity.[14] When the history of medicine and of the treatment of the mentally ill is analyzed from the therapeutic point of view, the Christian community must be described as a factor stifling therapy itself.[15] As the classical Greco-Roman medical tradition weakened, and the influence of the Christian churches grew, dark centuries in the care of mental illness began.[16]

Medical history has not put all of Christianity, especially Christianity when conformed to its original sources, in the dock of the accused[17] when it has analyzed the long dark period in the history of the therapeutic encounter with illness—a period described as having lasted 1,500 years.[18] What has been placed in the dock, however, is the Western formation of dogma, which played a destructive role in the history of the encounter with mental illness. Western dogma has been described as having had an injurious influence both on the formation of medical theories, and on the development of therapeutic methods based on empirical research.[19] From the therapeutic viewpoint, medical history has regarded the central trends in Western Christianity as phenomena which have retarded the development of therapy.[20] On the presuppositions for the Western Christian proclamation of the word and formation of community, it was not possible to share in or listen to the world of the mentally ill, nor was it possible to experience mental illness as an expression of a common, universal illness. History shows that those who understood mental illness and were its spokesmen came into sharp conflict with theological opinions;[21] and the mentally ill were often persecuted by churches.[22]

The history of Western Christianity viewed as therapy is quite different from that history viewed as prophecy. Medical history, on the one hand, points out that the establishment of Christianity in Western culture coincides with the period of the stultification of the therapeutic encounter with illness, "the dark centuries."[23] Church history, on the other hand, points out that Christianity has caused such a turning point in the history of the encounter with illness that in practice all care of the sick has received its impetus from the Christian proclamation of the word and establishment of community.[24] Regardless of the position one takes toward these different interpretations of history, their lack of agreement speaks clearly of a separation of therapy and prophecy. This split in the unity of therapy and prophecy persists and continues to bring about two different interpretations of history. In therapeutic circles one is often blind to both the historical and the immediate significance of prophecy in the therapeutic encounter with illness, and in the circle of prophecy one is inclined to exclude from church history the history of the encounter with illness.[25]

As therapy views illness in its communal aspect, it tends often to forget that the encounter with illness is also communal. There is a tendency in therapeutic studies to consider only the phenomena which are directly connected with medical care and with the development of hospitals as being relevant to the history of therapy. Other fronts of the encounter with illness in the life of communities—the common formation of symbols, for example—are ignored. It is understandable that an analysis of the history of therapy from such a narrow point of view, as though it had begun with the rise of "real" medical care, makes much of history appear dark.

From the viewpoint of prophecy alone, only the formation of words in churches and the development of organized churches is considered to be church history. The history of the encounter with illness is not considered to be an organic element in the history of Christian communities. Prophetic and therapeutic functions are viewed as separate and independent. Fulfillment of the prophetic function is thus considered to be possible without any organic correspondence with the therapeutic function. The history of the encounter with illness in Christianity, then, does not have any intrinsic meaning for the analysis of the history of prophecy and for an examination of its function. The voices which have arisen out of the midst of the encounter of illness with the perversions of our common life are irrelevant for prophecy whenever prophecy is thought to be formed independently of the reality of illness.[26]

This conflict between different interpretations of history becomes especially obvious in one phenomenon in the history of Western Christianity—the persecution of the mentally ill. In the therapeutic world increasing attention has been given to this phenomenon, especially as it appears in the Inquisition and in the persecution of witches. At the very time the analysis of Christian prophecy in medieval theology reached its high point in Thomas Aquinas' *Summa Theologica,* at the very time magnificent cathedrals arose as expressions of the development of Christian community, the leaders of the church officially confirmed the Inquisition. Pope Gregory IX gave it preliminary approval in 1233, and two decades later Pope Innocent IV confirmed the Inquisition as an official ecclesiastical institution. The history of therapy records the tragic influence of this institution upon the treatment of the mentally ill. Physicians and communities abandoned the mentally ill.[27] They were expelled from their homes to the streets, and doctors occupied themselves only with matters to which the influence of the Inquisition did not extend.[28] Thus, from the viewpoint of the therapeutic encounter with illness, the Inquisition in Western Christianity is a phenomenon which reveals the influence of prophecy on therapy. From this viewpoint, the isolation of the mentally ill and the Inquisition of the church are two sides of the same development. When one studies how mental illness became a stumbling block, and examines the way Christian community was established at the time of the Inquisition, one sees the place that Christian community takes in the history of the encounter with illness.

The Inquisition is thus one expression of the response of the church to illness. Even documents of the time regarded it thus. The Inquisition was considered—among other things—to be an institution whose goal was the healing and conquering of mental illness. The clearest example of this was the so-called Bible of Sorcery, *Malleus Maleficarum* ("The Witches' Hammer").[29] The authors were a chief inquisitor of Germany, Sprenger, and his assistant Kramer, both Dominicans. *Malleus Maleficarum* did not represent merely the opinions of its authors, since it received the official sanction of both secular and ecclesiastical officials.[30] Pope Innocent VIII promulgated a bull in 1484 which was appended to the book, authorizing these Dominicans to do their work in the name of the church. *Malleus Maleficarum* is a document of the church's encounter with mental illness.

Malleus Maleficarum is in many respects a significant book. It obviously represents an attempt to reach scientific objectivity. Its authors endeavored to verify its thesis by appealing to empirical research; their concern was to give evidence in terms of the science of their time for the existence of witchcraft.[31] On that basis, they then attempted to show that witchcraft was in irreconcilable conflict with the teachings and the life of the church.[32] The central purpose of Sprenger and Kramer was to show that the foundations of the Catholic faith could not be shaken even by those dangerous forces which they saw in the spreading of witchcraft and magic.[33] Witchcraft, numerous examples of which are given in the second chapter, involved essentially being in covenant with the devil. Those who deny the existence of witchcraft, *Malleus Maleficarum* states, are heretics, and more dangerous than the witches themselves. The Holy Scriptures show clearly that the devil does possess power over the body and mind of man when God gives him permission to use it. The witches have made a contract to obey the devil in all matters; whoever is under the spell of witchcraft is a blasphemer and must be treated as one.[34] An initial attempt must be made to convince such a person of his condition by various methods, as by prayers with him and for him, and by attempting to bring him into contact with the sacraments. One of the main methods described is exorcism by the power of words. When none of these methods has been successful, exercise of such tortures as the hot iron or the rack is recommended in order to pry out the confession necessary to expel the devil. If even this "shock treatment" fails, the stake remains the only therapeutic method of snatching a person away from the powers which are destroying his being.[35] The studies which describe the history of the encounter with mental illness state that in this way hundreds of thousands of mentally ill persons, mainly women, were burned as witches.

This burning was done on theological grounds in the framework of the official life of the church.[36]

The persecution of witches is thus, by its own account, a prophetic solution in a therapeutic situation. The brief description of the content of *Malleus Maleficarum* which we have presented points to a function which its authors considered themselves to be fulfilling, namely, therapy based on a prophetic foundation. The persecutors of witches tried to authenticate their work by appealing to the biblical writings and to the theological tradition of the church, and they believed they were meeting the symptoms of the sickness of their time in a genuinely therapeutic spirit. The institution of the Inquisition was for them the church's solution to mental illness.

The church's official solution, however, was not necessarily the most essential part of the encounter between the mentally ill and the medieval church, as is sometimes claimed in the descriptions of the treatment of the mentally ill. The description of the Middle Ages as a dark age in Western history usually tells more about the view of the historian than it does about medieval history. This is certainly so in the case of the interpretation of the history of the treatment of mental illness.[37] Medical history blinds itself to issues which would decisively alter the results of its study. Those who have examined the relation of the church to mental illness exclusively in terms of the persecution of witches have ignored the significance which many other activities of the church—for example, the sacrament of penance—have possessed in the encounter with illness.[38] Above all, the radiation of the work of the institutional church into the everyday life of individuals and communities is ignored. Obviously, in inexplicable and numerous ways this has involved a therapeutic encounter with mental illness.

If studies of the role of the medieval church in the encounter with mental illness see only the perseuction of witches, there will be blind spots also in regard to other periods of church history.[39] For example, the significance of the Reformation in the history of the encounter with mental illness has been almost totally ignored in many presentations of history.[40] It seems obvious, however, that Luther's monastic *Anfechtung* was a phenomenon akin to that which had earlier appeared both in the form of the persecution of witches and in the very witchcraft which was itself persecuted.[41] This kind of material receives no attention when the interpretation of the history of therapy is dominated by narrow "dogmatic" presuppositions.[42] Historians of medical therapy tend to view prophecy as one-sidedly as historians of prophecy view the place of therapy in both historical theology and church history. These latter historians fail to see the encounter with illness as part of church history.[43]

The way in which prophecy and therapy are mutually integrated and correlated in a common history is a multidimensional problem. Even if what we have described from the viewpoint of therapy has been very one-sided, it has drawn attention to the important question of the meaning of the phenomenon of persecution. Studies of prophecy have often avoided the impact of the persecutions which have occurred over the forming of prophetic words. The history of the encounter with mental illness points out that the treatment of the mentally ill in different eras is closely connected with the way the community forms its words and with the way the symbols of communion are administered. Here is one of the questions with which we must deal in our study. We are called to examine the Christian proclamation of the word and establishment of community in the perspective of discoveries in the therapy of mental illness—that stumbling block of life together.

3. The Voice of Illness Is Ignored

Having seen how the voice of illness has been stifled, we now turn to a second trend in the history of the encounter with illness which has been described in therapeutic studies as a tendency to ignore the psychological reality of illness and especially of mental

illness. This trend can be understood as having arisen during that
crisis of Western culture when the mystical and religious image of
the world was beginning to lose its influence and an attempt was
being made to build a new image of reality on the basis of empirical knowledge.[44]

According to this interpretation of history, the cultures which
became the sources of Western civilization—Greece, Palestine,
Egypt—regarded illness as a moral and religious reality. All the
agony of human life was seen as a consequence of breaking the
moral law.[45] Hence in those cultures illness meant a punishment
sent by the gods as a sign that man had consciously or unconsciously transgressed the laws of life. Illness and sin were seen as inseparably integrated realities. Any transgression of the laws of
life was rebellion against the gods, which the gods punished with
difficulties, disappointments, pain, and illness.[46]

Encounter with illness, then, implied studying the character of
those transgressions which had caused the illness. In the framework of Semitic culture, where the special character of the human
being as distinguished from nature in general was emphasized,
purification and release from transgressions was accomplished by
cleansing the sick person's conscience.[47] In the encounter with illness the central thing was the penitential cleansing of the conscience from sin and from mortal transgressions. In the Greek
world, the gods of nature and of men were seen to be intertwined
in a common destiny, and in dealing with transgressions, the attempt was made to listen to the oracles in which divine powers
were working in human nature. In the treatment of illness, the
main emphasis was on purification (*catharsis*) from those perversions of nature which the gods had sent as punishments for transgressions.[48]

Regardless of the differences to be seen in the understanding of
illness in these "mystical-religious" cultures, their common characteristic was the encountering of illness as a psychological reality.[49] When the main course of Western medicine began to take

shape in the midst of this cultural tradition, however, there occurred in the understanding of illness a radical departure from the
mythological tradition. The development began in Greek culture,
where students of nature (*physiologoi*) gathered the material for
theories of the structure of nature (*physis*). It was on this basis
that the first "natural" explanations of the character of illness were
built. *Corpus Hippocraticum* gathered and canonized views which
described illness as a phenomenon of nature.[50] Thus illness was
regarded in the Hippocratic tradition as a disturbance of the equilibrium which rules in nature.[51] In the treatment of illness the
aim was to find the natural causes of the disturbance and to restore the proper balance. The task of the physician was to be
"the servant of nature." He was required to understand the structure of nature and to seek immediate causes of illness in the human body, more remote causes in universal nature. The goal of
medical care was seen to be the healing or elimination of the sick
"elements" of the human organism, and this was to be based on a
knowledge of the structure of nature, a knowledge reached through
empirical research.[52] All forms in which illness appeared, both
physical and psychic, were to be studied as symptoms of disturbances in the human organism.

This Hippocratic outlook gradually became the main line of the
Western medical tradition, leading eventually to the tendency
which ignored illness as a psychological reality.[53] There were two
reasons for this avoidance: on the one hand, the dominance of the
tradition of Stoic thinking,[54] and on the other, the strengthening
of those tendencies which led to the persecution of the mentally
ill. This tendency to avoid the reality of mental illness became
finally established when the calm spirit of Arabic science gained
ascendancy in the world of medical care. The Arabic spirit, basing
its work on scientific methodology, was in sharp contrast with the
world of persecutions and demonological attitudes. This juxtapo-
sition of two parallel truths—truth received by faith and truth
gained by reason—was sharpened by the Arabic scientific tradi-

tion and provided the motivation for a division in the areas of treatment. During the persecutions, then, an attempt was made to leave the sickness of the mind to a treatment based on faith and to limit the treatment of illness to those physical ills which could be dealt with in empirical research.[55]

When this trend is viewed with therapy in mind, it is to be seen that the notion gradually developed that the soul belonged to the world of faith and the body to the world of reason. The care of souls began to be regarded as belonging to the church institution and to theology, the care of the body as belonging to hospitals and to medicine.[56] Illnesses of the mind were considered supernatural; illnesses of the body, natural. Bodily illness was viewed either as a mechanistic phenomenon separate from any relationship to God or, if viewed in terms of the salvation of the soul, as meaningful suffering; sickness of the mind, by contrast, was seen either as an irrational and meaningless phenomenon or as a sign of estrangement from God.

The mentally ill, if they were not persecuted, were put in "no man's land."[57] The only response to illness as a psychological reality was persecution,[58] and in all other respects mental illness was ignored as a phenomenon not congruent with the categories of the knowledge and experience of the time. That knowledge and experience understood the matter in a manner something like the following. The body was considered a machine which could be depicted graphically through empirical research, and illness could be explained as a disturbance of the machinery.[59] The voice of illness was then comparable to the noise of a faulty machine, alarming yet incoherent, possessing no consistent meaning. The noise, moreover, signalled a malfunction in the machine and aided in the location of that malfunction, or perhaps even showed that it was necessary to revise the design of the entire machine. In any case the noise itself had to be eliminated. Once the alarming noise was eliminated, it could be assumed that the machine was again in good repair. If this analogy is helpful, we can see that the human body was understood mechanistically, that is, as a machine which possessed a basic purpose and an appropriate manner of functioning. Illness was seen as a disturbance in the functioning of the bodily mechanism.

From this it is clear that the cause of illness was sometimes seen as indigenous and sometimes as exogenous, depending upon how the design of the bodily machinery was understood and which of its functioning centers was considered the most important.[60] Continuing this figure of speech, the encounter with illness could be closely compared to the repair of a machine—the fault had to be located and the broken part repaired or replaced, or if the fault were irreparable and the machine were not to be thrown away, means to function without the faulty part had to be discovered. In the encounter with illness the task was understood as the development both of materials to heal the sick part of the organism and of skills to replace sick parts. Different combinations of chemicals, useful in restoring proper balance to the body, and the skills of the surgeon, designed to excise and replace sick elements, were seen to be the decisive factors—even in the encounter with mental illness.[61]

In this way there gradually developed an image of reality which did not include mental illness as a psychological reality. There emerged an image of a normal reality dominated by laws which reason alone could grasp. Any development which could not be integrated with this reality was viewed as "abnormal." Now when the measure of normality is a physical reality seen in mechanistic categories, all abnormality is understood as a disturbance which must be either eliminated by some means or, in some extreme cases, endured. If mental illness is measured with this kind of standard, a therapeutic encounter with it becomes impossible.[62] Here the line between normal and abnormal is drawn on the basis of a concept of reality in which the psychical is relegated to a supernatural world, a world above physical reality, a world with its own laws. Regardless of how the relation between physical and psychical is understood, there remains no place on this ground for a therapeutic encounter with mental illness. If the sickness of the mind is believed to belong to the world of the soul, it cannot be treated as a sickness. The immortal soul cannot become sick. The illness, then, must be encountered with the methods of the care of souls, and the laws of supernatural reality must be pursued. If, however, mental illness is considered a physical phenomenon, it has to be studied and treated according to the laws of physical life.[63]

This tendency in the history of medical care to divide reality into the physical and the psychical is much more complicated than is usually thought. Whenever medical history speaks of this trend, it seems already to have answered the questions concerning the relationship of natural and supernatural, of faith and reason, of soul and body. It assumes that it has conquered the split which is expressed in the theory of two parallel truths. Therapeutic studies of the tendency toward persecution and of the tendency to ignore the reality of mental illness seem to say that the reason for both must be attributed to "dogmatism." It is implied, moreover, that this "dogmatism" can be replaced by empirical research.

The discernment of causes is a necessary stage in all study of history. In relation to the present discussion medical history locates the cause of the phenomena just examined in a complex of historical circumstances and in certain dogmatic ideologies. In any study of history, a selection of material based on given criteria is put into a cause-and-effect relationship. If in choosing the historical materials the researcher is conscious that the questions he uses in his choice are formed by the material he studies, and are thus themselves a part of the total cause-and-effect network, the choice of material and the locating of causes does not lead him to such an arbitrary interpretation of history as would otherwise be the case. In this kind of interpretation of history, the questions are revised continuously in the light of different factors in the interplay of historical forces.

Any interpretation of history which asks questions only in one way swiftly concludes that certain ages should be classified as "dark" and leads to a separation of the questions of the study from their historical connections. Whenever the historian believes that he is approaching history from a totally new viewpoint, many problems have been too easily eliminated from his studies. This is the temptation in the studies of therapy of which we have been speaking. The theory of the two parallel truths as analyzed in these studies, especially, has used such limited causal connections that many central problems concerning the split of Western consciousness disappear from the horizon.

The history of therapy, in interpreting the tendency to avoid the reality of mental illness, frequently places Christianity among the factors causing that split of mind which the therapeutic encounter with illness tries to heal. Therapy sees itself as repairing the split caused by prophecy. Regardless of the kernels of truth this view contains, it ignores the mutual interdependence of therapy and prophecy. A split in the organic unity of prophecy and therapy is revealed in any attempt to escape the stumbling block of mental illness; the therapeutic encounter with illness properly involves an integration of the therapeutic and prophetic functions. In the formulation of theories connected with the therapeutic encounter with illness one is participating in prophetic activity.[64] In therapy one cannot conquer the temptation to escape from the reality of mental illness merely by changing the methodology or by basing one's conclusions on experiences gained in therapeutic treatment only.

The dichotomy (two parallel truths, faith-reason, soul-body, supernatural-natural) which we are now questioning is an expression of a split in reality which has appeared in various forms throughout the development of Western culture. It is obvious, for example, that this bifurcation of reality has strongly influenced the tendency in our own culture to avoid a psychological view of illness. The tremendous rise of the natural sciences and the possi-

bilities they offer for man to rule over nature have strengthened
man's striving consciously to command the whole of human existence. When to technology is added the notion that man's consciousness of reality is identical to reality itself, man's reliance on
the possibilities of his conscious ego becomes almost unlimited.
When man regards his conscious ego, independent of other egos,
as the basic unit of reality, his central goal in life becomes the
domination of reality by enlarging the horizons of his consciousness and by gaining the power to realize the best interests of his
consciousness.[65] Illness then appears to man to be only a threat to
his existence, a threat which he must either escape or destroy.
Gradually there grows in consciousness an image of a healthy
"normal" reality where illness is only a disturbance.

Many different prophecies have tried to conquer this split of
consciousness—some religious, some philosophical, others based
on empirical research.[66] Christian prophecy is also called to proclaim its solution of the problem. In the therapeutic encounter
with illness, factors have been confronted which shed new light
upon that split of mind which has appeared in the encounter with
reality in Western Christianity. A basic theme in our investigation
is the message carried by illness itself concerning the nature of this
split. The view presented above provides the framework for this
investigation.

4.   The Voice of Illness Breaks Through

The tendency to stifle the voice of illness and the tendency to
ignore it have been described in anticipation of a third tendency
apparent in the history of the encounter with illness. This third
tendency, which is the most important for the present study, may
be called the therapeutic encounter with mental illness, or the
therapeutic tendency.

We must be careful not to overemphasize the special and revolutionary character of this third response to mental illness. To do

so would be to commit the error common to much historical interpretation of revolutionary phenomena whereby certain events
which have caused changes are placed in the center of history and
all other happenings are interpreted in their light. Psychological
research by individuals has given rise to various therapeutic schools
of thought, each of which presents its own interpretation of the
history of the encounter with illness. Common to most of these
schools is some "scientific psychology" regarded as having caused
a revolutionary turn in the understanding of human behavior. All
history before this revolution is viewed as only preparatory.

When in the following we analyze the study by therapeutic research of its own origins, we are not trying to present the history
of therapy. The purpose of this section is to examine the interpretations of history in the various therapeutic schools as they
have dealt with those questions which appear to them most central in the common history of prophecy and therapy. At the same
time the various interpretations of history will be seen as bringing
the picture of the third, or therapeutic, trend into clearer focus.
It is also important to emphasize that the various interpretations
by therapy of its own history as presented here will give only
some indication of the attempt of therapy to form a picture of
itself. Here the history of therapy will be viewed especially from
the viewpoint of the encounter with *mental* illness.

The challenge to realize selfhood as an individual takes a place
of special importance in the historical sources of the therapeutic
schools.[67] This is not surprising since in therapy healing is always
experienced as a deliverance of the sick from powers which en-
slave and pervert personal life.[68] It is therefore natural that the
standard bearers of individual freedom are seen as the pioneers of
the therapeutic tendency. Nevertheless, when historians of therapy
make their choices concerning these standard bearers, and when
they describe them, they often do so in such a poetic way—usually
Socrates is mentioned as the first real therapist—that such naming
of great men can in this connection be ignored.[69]

The therapeutic movement draws a clear picture of itself when it describes the factors which have immediately influenced its present structure. Here the humanistic movements of the Renaissance are presented as decisive. In these movements the structure of human nature became the object of study,[70] and thus the foundation was laid for the passion of the individual to become free from the perversions of nature.[71] Philosophical studies on the nature of man then became the basis on which empirical psychology could build and even though it was not until centuries later that this Renaissance "psychology" developed into an encounter with mental illness, the framework was thus prepared for a real encounter.[72] Similarly included in the legacy which Renaissance thinking left to therapy was the optimism with which man viewed his own potentiality for educating and healing himself.

The Renaissance is frequently described as a time when the dichotomous world-image of the Middle Ages began to give way to a new view which saw reality as a unity.[73] Man was understood as a microcosm in which different layers of reality confronted and melted into each other, and any split in reality was caused by the immaturity of man. The restoration of man meant the restoration of the whole reality.[74] To be sure, in the early Renaissance the Christ was identified as the saving microcosm—the real man.[75] The emphasis gradually, however, shifted so far that man himself became the divine microcosm.[76] Man, made in God's image, gathered in himself the elements to heal and renew the world. Man was both his own healer and the organism to restore the wholeness of split reality.[77]

This individualistic emphasis on the dignity of man has had social consequences of such a type that it has prepared the ground for the therapeutic encounter with illness.[78] One social consequence of Renaissance humanism has been the acceptance by society of responsibility for all of its members.[79] The Renaissance saw that in every man are hidden possibilities which wait for fulfillment, and that it is, therefore, really meaningful for society to

take care of all its members.[80] Thus the care of the sick acquired
philosophical motivation. Furthermore, Renaissance humanism encouraged psychology to experiment with various methods of treat-
ing the mentally ill. Gradually the point was reached where some
hospitals became mental hospitals and this was a decisive step on
the way toward the therapeutic encounter with illness.[81] Mental
hospitals initiated detailed clinical observations of the behavior of
the mentally ill: "the patient became the best textbook of the
physician."[82]

The voice of illness began to break through when mentally ill
persons in the community were acknowledged, even to a small degree, as members of that community. Illness was seen—in the
beginning only vaguely—as an illness of the community. Man began to speak of "the illness of the time" and "the illness of the
culture."[83] Mental illness was no longer greeted only as a supernatural threat, or a tragic disturbance of the natural course of life.
The suspicion arose that in the encounter with illness was hidden
the opportunity to detect, in the sick members of the community,
something of the character of the powers which disunite the community.[84] One began to see that conquest of the powers of illness
in the individual members of the community meant victory for
the whole society. An attempt was made to encounter the sickness
of the community in the sickness of the individual.

Humanistic tendencies, however, are not to be seen as the sole
starting point of the therapeutic encounter with illness. Alongside
them, naturalistic tendencies of thought which see an organic
unity between human nature and nature in its totality are acknowledged as important. It is often stated in studies of history
from the therapeutic point of view that naturalism not only is the
main cause of the development of the Western medical tradition,
but also an important cause of the break-through of the therapeutic encounter with mental illness.[85] This may seem surprising,
since these naturalistic trends have been described in the therapeutic interpretation of history as fatal for the encounter with mental

illness, and the main stream of the naturalistic medical tradition is believed to have avoided any encounter with illness as a psychological reality.

The history of therapy indicates that when the encounter with mental illness is based solely on the grounds of natural science the illnesses of the mind have been placed in the framework of the "supernatural," or they have been treated in the Procrustean bed of a mechanistic view of man. How then can this same naturalistic trend be seen as a factor which opens the way for encountering illness as a psychological reality? How is it possible to say that the therapeutic encounter with illness has grown from the ground prepared by the natural sciences, especially biology and physics?

The question of whether the humanistic trend or the naturalistic trend is central to the development of the therapeutic revolution is one of the principal points of division in the world of therapy.[86] The schools of thought which emphasize the "existential" character of the therapeutic encounter with illness generally consider the influence of the humanistic trend to be primary.[87] They say that the establishment of therapy on the basis of natural science, using scientific methods, is a phenomenon caused simply by certain accidental historical circumstances. In opposition to this, the therapeutic schools of thought which emphasize the scientific character of the therapeutic encounter with illness, and which build their theories on natural science, regard themselves as representing the classical tradition of therapy when they follow the naturalistic trend.[88] There are also other schools of thought which do not consider these humanistic and naturalistic trends in the history of therapy to be in fundamental opposition. They see in the therapeutic encounter with illness a synthesis of these trends.[89]

According to the existential view the dichotomy in the interpretation of reality (which first appears as a separation of the supernatural and natural, faith and reason, soul and body, and which therefore results in an escape from mental illness) is overcome in the humanistic approach. The humanistic interpretation of the nature of man means from this point of view the overthrow both of the theological tendencies which lead to the persecution of the mentally ill and of the mechanistic view of man which leads to an escape from the reality of mental illness. Therapy based on humanistic traditions seeks to restore that reality which previously was split in the tensions between theological and naturalistic forces.

From the contrasting viewpoint of the school which considers the naturalistic trend central in the history of therapy, humanistic therapy has gone only halfway in overcoming the dichotomy. From its viewpoint the natural sciences based on empirical research have first made it possible for therapy to become free from that dichotomous image of reality which has hindered its development. The natural sciences have gradually destroyed both the theological and the humanistic view of the structure of man.[90] They show that human nature is an organic part of that nature whose laws the natural sciences study. The natural sciences have created the foundation for a therapeutic encounter with illness in which dichotomous interpretations of reality do not pervert therapy but in which, rather, therapy follows the laws of nature.

According to the third view, which tries to reach a synthesis between humanistic and naturalistic tendencies, any break-through in the therapeutic encounter with illness demands that theological, humanistic, and naturalistic tendencies in the history of therapy become organically intertwined. When from this viewpoint it is emphasized that naturalistic trends and the natural sciences have prepared the way for the therapeutic encounter with illness, it is meant that they have contributed to the preparation of the synthesis. The tendency, in the naturalistic approach, to study and to treat man as an organic part of the totality of nature does not necessarily lead to a mechanistic view of man, nor does it necessarily hinder an encounter with illness as a psychological reality, unless the approach is dominated by mechanistic interpretations of nature. When the unity of man and nature is really seen in an organic way, the study of nature and the analysis of its laws are inseparably integrated with the study of man. The study of nature is always essentially humanistic. If human nature is seen as integrated in a definite way with the totality of nature, its study is always naturalistic. Thus the natural sciences are a part of that study which deals with illness as a psychological reality.

To summarize, in an analysis of the common history of prophecy and therapy from the therapeutic point of view, trends are to be discerned which have a decisive significance in the mutual correspondence of prophecy and therapy. These trends are characterized by the terms theological, naturalistic, and humanistic. The theological views of illness are frequently described as directly stifling the therapeutic encounter with illness. Radically naturalistic interpretations of illness are also seen as obstacles to the growth of therapeutic trends. In fact, it is often the case that only the humanistic tradition is regarded as containing such elements as directly open a way for the therapeutic encounter.

Perhaps one essential reason for such an image of therapy is that these three tendencies appear so strongly in the break-through of the therapeutic encounter with illness. Descriptions of the break-through by the various schools of thought differ, of course, but all three traditions are in agreement that the revolution has brought a crisis in the mutual relationships of theology, naturalism, and humanism. The break-through of the therapeutic encounter with illness has been seen as the final collapse of theological interpretations of man. It has also been interpreted as the liberation of authentically Christian views from the bonds of those "dogmatic" opinions which have enslaved them for centuries. Some see in the therapeutic revolution the final victory of naturalism over the metaphysical interpretations of humanism and theology, while others consider it to mean that humanism has overcome the mechanistic view of naturalism and the dogmatic view of theology.

Chapter 3

The Therapeutic Encounter
with Illness

1. Listening to the Voice of Illness

The three movements which we have described as having played decisive roles in the origins of the therapeutic encounter with illness (theology, naturalism, and humanism) were genuinely intertwined in the theories of Sigmund Freud, the central figure in the therapeutic "revolution."[1] On the one hand, he radically dismissed theological trends because, in his opinion, they both stifled the healing of the sick and were theoretically meaningless. On the other hand, however, Freud entered into such deep communion and encounter with the sick that his expressions for conveying the message of illness were "theological." We have only to look at Freud's attempts to form, on the basis of his experiences in therapy, a prophetic interpretation of the structure of the whole historical panorama. In some respects his interpretation of history was obviously *heilsgeschichtlich,* an interpretation of history from the viewpoint of healing and salvation. On the basis of his therapeutic experiences, he built a theory of the original nature of man (*justitia originalis,* "the paradise") and of the loss of this nature through a process of estrangement ("the fall into sin"). The therapeutic encounter with illness he understood as a victory over those powers which have estranged man from his real nature ("salvation"). This analysis has the same structure as that biblical prophetic interpretation of history in which experiences of salvation are the starting point in viewing the history of the whole of mankind. Freud analyzed history as a history of salvation in which the powers which destroy and restore life are in conflict.[2]

A similar mixture of diverse elements can be seen in Freud's attitude toward humanistic and naturalistic influences on therapy. Freud said, on the one hand, that the natural sciences provided the key to understanding the character of illness, often expressing himself in categories of a mechanistic natural science.[3] On the other hand, Freud argued strongly that a mechanistic scientific view of man is one of the highest barriers to the therapeutic encounter with illness. Freud seemed also to draw richly from the sources of humanism, especially from the world of Greek drama.

In Freud's own view his sources were only apparently divergent and he never would have agreed that a combination of conflicting sources had taken place. That he did in fact harmonize previously conflicting elements clearly illustrates how multidimensional is the occasion when illness is encountered and listened to as a psychological reality, and the message conveyed to the whole community organism. Then it is that one fulfills the prophetic function of therapy. Then it is that the therapeutic encounter with illness leads to a confrontation with the principal movements which build the spirit of the time.

In any given moment of history, the attitudes a community forms toward illness reveal the attitudes of that community toward all of the basic questions of human existence.[4] The encounter with illness mirrors the image of man in a given era. In the encounter it becomes apparent on what kind of prophecy the community is building, accordingly as the voice of illness is stifled, avoided, or heeded. Obviously, theological, humanistic, and naturalistic tendencies gain ascendancy during certain eras and provide for a limited encounter with illness, yet particular tendencies such as these remain prevalent only when the encounter with illness is so petrified that no deep level of penetration is reached.

In the history of the encounter with mental illness the way in which any given group of people becomes an integrated or a disintegrated organism is clearly revealed in its encounter with illness. If, for example, in the lore of the community organism the majority of the members consider themselves "healthy" and persecute or isolate the "sick" members, the prophecy which grows up in this community and its general use of symbols gradually conform to this constellation of values. When in such a situation the attempt is made to listen to the voice of illness and to convey its message to those who have fortified themselves in the position of the "healthy," a process begins which influences all of the functions of the common organism. Listening to the voice of illness shakes those positions which have been gained through an isolation of the reality of illness.[5]

"It was one of the momentous turns in the history of medical psychology when Freud, having decided to use hypnotism, stood before his patient reary to read out of him that which the patient knew but of which he was unaware."[6] The central content of the therapeutic revolution can be stated briefly: one is alerted in the encounter with illness to listen to the voice of illness. In the encounter with illness it becomes essential to study the language through which the illness expresses its meaning and content. Freud himself has expressed this: "One day the discovery was made that the symptoms of disease in certain nervous patients have meanings. It was upon this discovery that the psychoanalytic method of treatment was based."[7]

2.   Man Is Encountered in Illness

The basic character of the discovery made in listening to the voice of illness is more important, from the viewpoint of our theme, than the theories which were later built around it. There is, of course, a correspondence between the basic experience in therapy and the theory based on it, but it is a mistake to think that theories as such express the essential intentions of that experience upon which they are founded. It is not at all self-evident, for example, that Freud's theories of religion and culture are derived from his basic therapeutic experiences. In any case, an analysis of the different theories presented by Freud cannot be substituted for the study of the basic character of his encounter with and his hearing of the voice of illness.[8] It has been well said of Freud:

> But for all the Hebraic quality, Freud is also in the classical tradition—combining the Stoics and the great Greek dramatists. For as for the Stoics, there is no possibility of man disobeying the laws of nature. And yet, it is in this lawfulness that for him the human drama inheres. His love for Greek drama and his use of it in his formulation are patent. The sense of human tragedy, the inevitable working out of the human plight—these are the hallmarks of Freud's case histories. When Freud, the tragic dramatist, becomes a therapist, it is not to intervene as a directive authority. The therapist enters the drama of the patient's life, makes possible a play within a play, the transference, and when the patient has "worked through" and understood the drama, he has achieved the wisdom necessary for freedom.[9]

What it means to listen to the voice of illness in such a way that its most delicate nuances are heard, and the sick one is met in the depths of his illness, becomes clear in the case history of one of Freud's first patients:

> In the fall of 1892 I was requested by a friendly colleague to examine a young lady who had been suffering from pains in her legs for over two years, so that she walked badly. He also added to his request that he had diagnosed the case as hysteria, though none of the usual symptoms of the neurosis could be found. He stated that he knew very little of the family, but that the last few years had brought them much misfortune and little pleasure. First the patient's father died, then the mother underwent a serious operation on her eyes, and soon thereafter a married sister succumbed to a chronic cardiac affection following childbirth. Our patient had taken an active part in all the afflictions, especially in the nursing of the sick.[10]

Elizabeth was twenty-four years old when she came under Freud's care. She was "intelligent and psychically normal." Freud first vividly tells in his case study of his attempts to locate the causes for the pains in her legs. Gradually he moves on step by step, listening to the language of the illness of the patient, and drawing a sensitive picture of Elizabeth's life.

Elizabeth was the youngest of three daughters, and she had lived her youth with her parents, whom she admired, on their estate. The health of the mother was unstable. She had an eye infection and she was nervous. Elizabeth was especially fond of her warm-hearted and open-minded father. The father, although he enjoyed having her as a companion, warned his daughter that she was not developing womanly characteristics, and expressed the opinion that it would be difficult for her to find a husband. When the family moved to the capital, Elizabeth was refreshed at first by the richer opportunities of social life Vienna offered. However, the father soon developed an illness quite unexpectedly. He was brought home unconscious, suffering from a serious heart condition. Elizabeth took care of him tirelessly for a year and a half, sleeping in his room, waking in the night to help him, and serving him every day. The first memories of pains in her legs were from that period. Two years after the death of her father, Elizabeth began to feel that she was too ill to walk.

After the death of the father, the life of the family of four women became difficult in many respects. Elizabeth sought consolation by trying to concentrate on the care of her mother, who became more and more infirm. The oldest sister married at the end of the year of mourning, marrying an able and ambitious man of good social standing. This brother-in-law, however, soon showed an antipathy toward his mother-in-law, and this proved unbearable to Elizabeth. In every case she defended her mother against her brother-in-law, being obviously disappointed that the family did not have a harmony for which she longed. The marriage of the second sister offered more promise. While the second brother-in-law was not so gifted as the first, his cordial behavior melted the negative attitude which Elizabeth had originally had toward marriage. This couple also remained near the mother, and its child became Elizabeth's favorite.

Unfortunately the mother's eye infection grew worse before the favorite child was a year old. The mother had to remain for weeks in a dark room where Elizabeth cared for her faithfully. After a successful eye operation, all three families arranged to spend their summer together at a vacation resort. There Elizabeth, who had hoped to use this time for a much-needed rest, herself fell ill and became the patient of the family. The physician prescribed health baths; Elizabeth hesitated to remain away from home, because her sister was again pregnant and Elizabeth was anxious about her condition. She and her mother had not been at the spa more than two weeks when they received word to return home. When they arrived, Elizabeth's sister was already dead.

Elizabeth not only suffered because of the loss of her beloved sister, but also because of the thoughts it aroused in her mind, and because of the changes which the death caused in the life of the family. Since the sister had succumbed to a heart disease aggravated by pregnancy, the relatives accused themselves of not having tried to prevent the marriage and their accusing thoughts were also directed toward the widower. Above all Elizabeth was depressed because her mother's life became more and more solitary. The widower withdrew himself and his child into the circle of his own family. Thus for the next year and more, Elizabeth was almost totally isolated from the rest of the world as she concentrated herself entirely on the care of her mother.

After having gone this far, Freud states that what Elizabeth has told him has not given him any real insight concerning the causes of the illness or any hints for its care:

> One could not conceive what beneficial influence Miss Elizabeth could derive from recounting sad, familiar family experiences of the past years to a stranger, who could give her in

> return only moderate sympathy, nor could one observe any im-
> provement after the confession . . . Had I given up the patient
> at this stage of the psychic treatment, the case of Miss Eliza-
> beth v. R. would have been of no importance whatever for the
> theory of hysteria. But I continued my analysis . . .[11]

In the continued analysis new levels of insight began to appear.
The patient remembered an evening when a young man had ac-
companied her home, and she recalled her own feelings when she
then went back to caring for her father. She and the young man
were fond of each other, but Elizabeth decided that evening—after
having seen that her father's condition was worse—that she would
never again leave him alone for a whole evening. The young people then saw each other less frequently and gradually their ways
parted. In this relationship, and in the conflicts which Elizabeth
experienced through it, Freud sought the reasons for the young
woman's first hysterical pains. The conflict between the happiness
which Elizabeth at first had not denied herself and the sad condition in which she found her father became insoluble. According
to Freud, Elizabeth removed her erotic desires from consciousness,
and the effect of this suppression was to heighten the physical pain
which had appeared at the same time. That which could and
should have caused psychic afflictions was converted into physical
pains (the defense mechanism of conversion).

Although the moment of this first "conversion" had not yet
become clear, its motivation had been found. After some time
Elizabeth surprised her doctor by saying that she knew why the
pains were felt more severely in her right leg. The father's leg
had leaned against her leg every morning as she changed his band-
ages. This had not occurred to her earlier, but from then on Elizabeth's painful legs always "participated in the discussion." Often
the pain became more severe when Elizabeth tried to recall forgotten things. She would then put her hand on that area where
the pain was felt most severely. Freud states that he gradually
learned to use these pains as a compass,[12] and more and more the

causes of the pains came to light. It was increasingly apparent that Elizabeth had been seeking a symbolic expression for her afflicted thoughts and that she had found it in creating physical pains. As the treatment went further the resistance of the patient grew stronger.

The third stage of treatment began when one event gave Freud the opportunity to test a hypothesis which had entered his mind. One day when he was working with his patient, Freud tells of hearing a man's steps in the next room, and a man's voice speaking in a pleasant way. Elizabeth stood up immediately and asked Freud to stop the treatment for that day. Elizabeth had just heard her brother-in-law come in and ask for her. Just before this disturbance the patient had been free from pain, but soon after this event especially severe pains reappeared.

After some time, Elizabeth remembered some associations from the vacation resort where she had been before she left for the health spa. Exhausted by the care of her mother, she began to feel desperate over being an unmarried woman whose life lacked fulfillment and who was unable to reach her own goals. Until that time she had thought herself strong enough to live without a man, but at that moment she became preoccupied with a feeling of womanly weakness and with a desire for love. (Elizabeth stated that when she remembered this her "hardened ego" began to melt.) In that state of mind the happy marriage of her sister made a strong impression, and Elizabeth remembered how lovingly her brother-in-law had taken care of her sister and how a mere glance was enough to express the mutual understanding of the young couple. Elizabeth remembered also how her brother-in-law at first had not wanted to accompany her on the walk during which her pains first began to appear serious. He had wanted to remain at home with his sick wife, but with a glance she had encouraged her husband to go, thinking that it would bring Elizabeth pleasure. During the walk there developed between Elizabeth and her brother-in-law a lively and warm discussion. Elizabeth recalled how her mind was overwhelmed with the desire to find a man like her brother-in-law. Later, on the morning when she left for the health spa, Elizabeth returned to the place where they had walked together, and there, looking out on the beautiful view, she sat down on a stone and thought of her sister's happiness and dreamed of a man like her brother-in-law, a man who could understand her. After standing up she felt in her legs severe pain which disappeared for a moment, then returned and remained permanent. Freud continues:

> For some time the state of affairs must have been clear to me. The patient seemed absorbed in painfully sweet recollections, so that she was wholly unconscious of the drift of her thoughts and continued to reproduce her reminiscences. She spoke of the time in Gastein, the worry connected with the expectation of her letter, finally the information of her sister's illness, the long wait until the evening when she could finally leave Gastein, the journey with its tormenting uncertainties during a sleepless night—all these moments were accompanied by a violent aggravation of the pain. I asked her if during the journey she thought of the sad possibility which she afterward found realized. She answered that she carefully avoided the thought, but that in her opinion her mother expected the worst from the very beginning. This was followed by the reminiscences of her arrival in Vienna . . . the short journey from Vienna to the neighboring summer resort where her sister lived, the arrival in the evening, the hasty walk through the garden to the door of the little garden pavilion—a silence in the house, the oppressive darkness, the fact of not having been received by the brother-in-law. She then recalled standing before the bed seeing the deceased and in the moment of the awful certainty that the beloved sister had died without having taken leave of them and without having her last days eased through their nursing—in that very moment another thought flashed through Elizabeth's brain, which now peremptorily repeated itself. The thought which flashed like dazzling lightning through the darkness was "Now he is free again, and I can become his wife."[13]

Freud states that from this moment he as therapist experienced great difficulty. The return of the thought which Elizabeth had suppressed from consciousness was to the "poor child" a shattering experience. When Freud told her that she had been in love with her brother-in-law for a long time, Elizabeth complained that she experienced the most terrible pains. She tried to reject the explanation, saying that Freud had invented it. She, Elizabeth, was incapable of such base thoughts. She would never be able to forgive herself for this. However, Freud showed her that there was no other explanation for what she had described, consoling her by saying that she was not responsible for her feelings, and that her behavior, her sickness in this circumstance, witnessed to the moral power of her character.[14] Freud reports, however, that it took a long time before these consolations made any impression on Elizabeth.

Now new levels of Elizabeth's consciousness began to appear. The first time that the future brother-in-law had visited the sister's home he had mistakenly greeted Elizabeth first, thinking that she was his bride-to-be. Once the sister had found Elizabeth and her future husband in such a lively and warm discussion that she had half-seriously exclaimed, "You two really belong together." A number of such memories made it gradually clear to Elizabeth that she had been very fond of her brother-in-law, perhaps from their very first meeting.

Elizabeth began gradually to regain her health: "We both felt," Freud states, "that the work had been finished."

> I urged her to bear calmly the uncertainties of her future which could not be dismissed . . . I regarded her as cured and urged her to continue independently the solution . . . In the spring of 1894 I was informed that she would be present at a private ball to which I could gain access. I did not let the opportunity escape me and saw my former patient gliding along in a rapid dance. Since then, following her own inclination, she married a stranger.[15]

3. Illness Is Encountered in Man

In order to understand the revolutionary character of this episode we must recall an insight we have previously drawn from the wells of the history of the encounter with illness. Men—and especially women—with sick minds had through the centuries been persecuted, or at the least excluded from medical care. Now a hysterical woman, Elizabeth, becomes the object of careful listening and study. The encounter with illness takes place through listening to the voice of illness, and the therapy is seen in terms of dialogue.

The unique character of this episode becomes especially clear if we compare it with the manner in which illness was encountered in the persecution of witches. In some respects the encounters between the torturer and the witch which are described in documents dealing with the persecution of witches remind us of what transpired in our episode between the therapist and the patient. Freud wrote to a friend shortly after our episode:

> By the way, what have you got to say to the suggestion that the whole of my brand-new theory of the primary origins of hysteria is already familiar and has even been published a hundred times over, though several centuries ago? Do you remember me always saying that the medieval theory of possession, that was held by the ecclesiastical courts, was identical with our theory of a foreign body and the splitting of the consciousness?[16]

In the same connection Freud also pointed out how the therapist in some respects acts as inquisitor. The patient must go through agonies similar to those of the tortured witches. Both the inquisitor and the therapist encounter illness as a psychological reality, the difference becoming apparent in the way the encounter takes place.

In the account of Elizabeth's therapy we can trace the destruction of the barriers which had hindered the break-through of the voice of illness. As the illness began to speak, it disrupted the positions both of the patient and of the therapist. Freud remarked of this case study:

> I have not always been a psychotherapist, but like other neuropathologists I was educated to methods of focal diagnosis and electrical prognosis, so that even I myself am struck by the fact that the case histories which I am writing read like novels, and as it were, dispense with the serious features of the scientific character. Yet, I must console myself with the fact that the nature of the subject is apparently more responsible for this issue than my own predilection.[17]

Listening to the illness led to a new way of forming words both for the patient and for the therapist. The image which the patient forms of himself and his reality, his interpretation or "prophecy" of his life's history and content, appears to be an essential element in illness. The cure of Elizabeth was effected by breaking such an image. In the same way, the therapist has to recognize that he is one element of the sick situation within which he is seeking ways of healing. Freud experienced the breaking of those measures and classifications which he had used in encountering illness; he was required to leave his position as an observer and become a listening "fellow patient." Listening to illness leads to a dialogue between the patient and the therapist in which both must assume new positions. In the therapeutic encounter with illness one is in fact in a prophetic situation; neither the patient nor the therapist possesses criteria adequate for moving from sickness to health until he first listens to the voice of illness.

In his analysis of Elizabeth's case, Freud also concentrates on a study of what happens between the therapist and the sick person. He says later that the most essential objects of psychoanalytic studies are those "transference neuroses" which are experienced in the encounter between the therapist and the patient.[18] The therapeutic encounter with illness has made him recognize that men can have a relationship more far-reaching than mere communication. The dialogue which grows in therapy demonstrates that words as such do not create communion between people. A merely sympathetic hearing of the patient does not lead to an encounter with the reality of illness nor does listening in itself serve as the method of treatment. Listening is in fact the basic problem in therapy. A healing dialogue cannot grow between the therapist and the patient without a deep crisis in both. The formation of words both by the patient and by the therapist is at every moment in danger of becoming diabolic, of breaking down the communion-like healing encounter. A symbolic formation of words which can create communion is possible only if both participants become aware of the factors which stifle real listening; they must let the reality of illness speak.

The transference between the therapist and the patient experienced in the encounter with illness appears to be of such a character that both participants are pulled into the whirlpools of becoming ill and becoming well. In his earliest work, Freud notes that the therapist, with his words, is placed in the world of the patient, where he must endeavor to treat the patient.[19] Therefore Freud emphasizes again and again that the encounter between the patient and the therapist must of necessity be analyzed in a most careful way.[20] If the therapist accepts the role of the "helper" where the patient tries to put him, the blind is leading the blind. The reality of illness and its hidden message is not encountered if the therapist takes the role of the healer. A healing dialogue in the encounter with illness can grow only if both the patient and the therapist concentrate on listening together to the voice of illness. The therapy has to take place in extreme privation, *in extremer Versagung*.[21] In the encounter with illness the two participants cannot remain in the position of simply responding to each other's fears and wishes. It is necessary to concentrate on listening to the language of illness as it appears in the behavior of the human organism.

In each human organism there is a unique forming of words

which, properly heard, reveal the reality peculiar to that person. Indeed, the whole behavior of man symbolizes the structure of his own being as it is understood, for example, from the biological point of view.[22] This does not mean, however, that man as a psychological reality can be explained in the light of any theory of "natural law." "The nature of man" is that which is revealed as nature and becomes symbolized in the different human organisms. It is not proper to speak of human nature apart from individual human organisms. The reality of human nature is discovered only by listening to what the different human organisms are saying; it is in the symbolic mutual dialogue between human organisms that human nature is revealed.

Experiences in therapy show that every man becomes sick and healthy in his own individual way. Every human organism cuts its own path to death and life. It is possible to speak of human nature only after listening to the man. If the therapist tries in his encounter with illness to follow some specific theory of human nature or to cast the sick person in the mold of a certain "real man," he becomes deaf to the message of illness in the structure of human existence. Thus Booth writes:

> To breed a model "healthy human race" is about as realistic as breeding a "basic dog." Any human health breeder would have to jump over his own shadow of specific idiosyncrasies before he could even set up a sound theory for such a program.[23]

4. Illness and the Word

It may seem strange to emphasize the central significance of the forming of words in therapy when it is a commonplace that in therapy the encounter with unconscious factors has assumed a basic role. Freud, for example, claims that one of the chief reasons for the fact that psychoanalysis has become a stumbling block in our culture is the emphasis it has placed on unconscious reality.[24] According to Freud, "the identification of the psychic and conscious" has in our culture become such a self-evident starting point for understanding man that the thesis of the influence of "unconscious reality" upon the "psychic life" of man is seen as directly shattering the foundations of our culture.[25] One may ask: If the behavior of man is mainly determined by unconscious factors, how can the forming of words be an essential element in man's illness and recovery?[26] Could it not be said, conversely, that the conscious life of man is meaningless in his getting sick or well? If man is directed by unconscious drives, how can the decisions or indecision of his conscious ego influence his illness and recovery? Is it not inconsequential to concentrate on verbal therapy if the behavior of man is determined by unconscious reality?

Questions concerning the role of the unconscious life in man's illness or health have become especially controversial in therapy. Different therapeutic schools are in wide disagreement.[27] There are schools which reject entirely Freud's view and say that his concept of unconscious reality represents a return to the mechanistic view of man.[28] There are also schools which reject Freud's theories as morally suspect: his strong emphasis on unconscious factors takes the ground out from under ethical responsibility and a healthy consciousness of guilt.[29] Many schools of thought consciously try to follow Freud's theories but they differ in interpretation. In the following we are concerned only with those thoughts of Freud and the various therapeutic schools which speak of the mutual relationship of unconscious and conscious reality and which lead to an emphasis on the central significance of the forming of words in therapy.

In discussions of the mutual relationship of unconscious and conscious life, not enough attention has hitherto been paid the fact that "unconscious" and "conscious" are not fixed concepts. There is no agreement as to their content, and they mean different things in different systems of thought. For example, when the psyche is identified with consciousness (as Freud claimed was characteristic of the theories of his time) and the instincts are regarded as unconscious reality, one often discerns, especially in Freud's own writing, an emphasis on man's instinctual life at the expense of his conscious life. Freud does not solve this problem, but he couches it in new terms. He rejects both the identification of the psyche with consciousness and the characterization of unconscious reality as instinctual.[30] The behavior of man has to be viewed as a psychological whole, and unconscious and conscious are for Freud expressions of the character of this total behavior. The most central decisions—from the viewpoint of man's illness and health—happen in that which the human organism represses into the unconscious or allows to come into the conscious. It is here also that the perversion and clarification of the forming of words takes place.

> In order to make it easier to understand this "compulsion to repeat" . . . we must above all get rid of the mistaken notion that what we are dealing with in our struggle against resistances is resistance on the part of the *unconscious*. The unconscious—that is to say, the "repressed"—offers no resistance whatever to the efforts of the treatment. Indeed, by itself it has no other endeavor than to break through the pressure weighing down on it and to force its way either to the consciousness or to a discharge through some real action. Resistance during the treatment arises from the same higher strata and systems of the mind which originally carried out repression . . . We shall avoid a lack of clarity if we make our contrast not between the conscious and the unconscious but between the coherent *ego* and the *repressed*. It is certain that much of the ego is itself unconscious . . .[31]

When the unconscious is described in this way it becomes immediately clear that the forming of words is of crucial importance for the entire human organism and especially for its conscious behavior. Man's psychic life is seen to possess a structure which is formed in the interplay of the forces of the whole human organism.

As we seek to explain the inner logic of the new emphasis on the significance of the "word" in therapy and the new understanding of the way in which the conscious ego of man is built up, it is necessary to remember the background of the therapeutic encounter with illness. When we analyzed the views which influenced the encounter with illness in former eras, we stated that the distinction between the psychic and the physical has been an obstacle to encountering illness as a psychological reality. In this context, when theological tendencies dominate, illness is encountered either under the banner of the "care of souls," in which case the conscious life and the forming of words are considered central, or the sick are left to experts who deal only with the mechanism of the body.[32]

The humanistic tendency gave the impression that the psychic has its own laws alongside those of the physical. The "psychic reality" is independent of illness and health; "reason," the conscious ego of man, cannot become sick. The disturbances which eventually appear in reason are due to the fact that the mechanisms of the body are out of order. According to the naturalistic view, man's conscious life and the forming of words by the human organism have no essential influence on man's becoming sick or well.

In the authentic therapeutic encounter, on the contrary—as the episode from Freud's work has shown—the behavior of the human organism is experienced as a unit. In therapy, both verbal and nonverbal expressions of the sick organism are watched attentively, even the nuances that are thought to be insignificant. Together these are regarded as one meaningful language. The fact that this language is heard is the basic factor in healing.

When the human organism is conceived as a unity, and both the verbal and nonverbal expressions of its conscious and unconscious life are seen to have grown out of the same event, not only does the forming of words take on new emphasis, but the very character of such forming of words is seen in a new light. We pointed this out earlier when we stated that the symbolic character of the forming of words is emphasized in therapy. When the conscious life is conceived as a psychical reality with its own laws distinct from physical reality, verbal and nonverbal experiences and expressions of the human organism have no organic connection.[33] If, in the formation of human behavior, conscious life is seen as an unessential surface of biological behavior, the relationship of verbal and nonverbal elements is also conceived as accidental and mechanistic. When the forming of words is called symbolic, however, we imply that the whole experience of the human organism influences the forming of words and the entire conscious life. The functions of consciousness are then no longer examined as "spiritual" functions with their own laws[34] or as spiritual reflections of some areas of the organism (e.g., the brain); rather, in such functions the human organism as a whole is seen to be expressing itself. One cannot locate any particular section of the reality of the human organism as the field where the powers of the conscious life of man play.[35] Conscious life, in structure and in content, is an expression of the whole existence of man.[36]

Listening to the voice of illness raises the question of the meaning for the prophetic function of that protest which illness makes against the way health has been traditionally understood and realized. Furthermore, we are led to analyze life as a prophetic situation lived under the pressure of the dynamic between illness and health. The reality of illness persuades us to take a listening attitude and to engage in a dialogue in our performance of the prophetic function.[37]

5.   The Communal Nature of Illness

The case history of Elizabeth von Ritter is a detailed study, not only of the sickness of a particular individual, but also of the sickness of that community organism in which the individual organism had become so entangled that she could not walk. This episode seems to indicate that a destructive, diabolical formation of words occurs when one human organism is isolated from other human organisms. The healing formation of words is experienced when man encounters man.

In recent years therapeutic research has developed a view of reality as a community organism like the view we glimpsed in the episode of Elizabeth as Freud analyzed it. In this section we will examine some of the questions which confront us in the light of pertinent "sociopathological" studies.

Sociopathology emphasizes strongly that the relationships between human organisms and their environment are organic even as the members of an individual organism are organically interrelated.[38] In a word, men form a community organism; we are "members one of another."[39]

In the history of the therapeutic encounter with illness there have been many developments pointing in this direction. Some of these we have already reviewed. In Freud's study of Elizabeth we saw that in their encounter both therapist and patient had to be integrated into the community organism in a new way. The dimensions of the illness which manifested themselves as a paralysis of the patient's legs could not be limited only to a certain area in the organism. The healing of the legs occurred only when the patient's whole being was integrated in a new way into the community organism. For his part, the therapist was forced to revise the categories of sickness which the community had established; otherwise he would have been required to resign himself to the sick situation which he shared with his patient.[40]

In the therapeutic encounter with illness a decisive role is played not only by the therapist and the patient, but also, quite commonly, by the patient's closest relatives. One has to deal with the fact that relatives begin to resist the healing of the sick in cases where healing means for them a challenge to revise their own posture.[41] In the therapy of schizophrenia, for example, we encounter the "schizophrenia" of the different cultural forms of that community where the illness manifests itself.[42]

Studies of the behavior of hospitalized children point in the same direction. In many cases the satisfaction of physical and chemical needs does not help if the child is not at the same time receiving the opportunity to be integrated into the vital human relationships which are necessary for him.[43] Likewise, studies of the life of concentration camps describe the human relationship as "symbiotic."[44]

Studies of speech defects in those who have brain injuries are particularly instructive. They show that words are not merely a means of communication through which the individual is in contact with his environment; rather, words are an organic part of that framework through which the individual organism becomes integrated into the community organism.[45] These same studies have also emphasized that man's preoccupation with his own self-preservation is pathological.[46] As the human organism becomes healthy it seeks to realize itself through integration in its individual way into the community organism. Therefore, if man is studied only in his isolation from the community organism, erroneous conclusions will follow similar to those which result from studies in which the organs of the human body are treated as isolated from the whole.[47] The behavior of an organ when isolated is dissimilar to its behavior in its organic environment. Studies of the pathology of thought, consequently, emphasize that "the mind is a function of two or more brains and not the property of one."[48]

In the analysis of many illnesses which were earlier studied only from the physical and chemical viewpoint, for example, cancer, arthritis, and Parkinson's disease, attention has recently been given to the symbolic character of becoming ill. In these diseases something of the interrelation between the individual organism and the community organism is manifested.[49] Studies are presently being made of the variations of the spread of a disease such as cancer[50] in different cultures and in different layers of the same culture.[51] In studies of "unexplained" death it is now common to speak of social death.[52] In psychology a theory of "a social ego" has been developed according to which the human person is formed in a symbolic mutual interaction, in a "society of egos."[53]

The world as a reality where men are integrated one with another (Buber: *Zwischenmenschlichkeit*) has also become an object of special interest to philosophical doctrines of man. The individual human person comes into existence in an encounter between Me and Thee; human existence is seen in its basic structure as dialogical.[54] The specific character of human existence is manifest in that men not only form collective groups, but also become integrated into unique community organisms.

In such connections it has been emphasized that there is an essential difference between man's becoming integrated into the community organism and his forming of a "society" or "group." Men can be members of a society or group without encountering one another as men, without being in a specifically human relationship with one another. Even an integrated group can be entirely disintegrated as a community organism. A certain kind of group unity can directly stifle specifically human, communion-like unity.[55] For example, the unity which grows out of social groups tends to become collective, the group and its interests and goals becoming central and the members of the group becoming means through which the group achieves its goals. Unity is then experienced not as the human interaction of the members but as a collective reality which subsumes the members and stands independent of them.[56]

In sociological research the categories used to describe "society" and "group" are also generally employed in describing the reality of illness. Sociology seldom examines illness as a reality affecting the whole community organism.[57] Social theories usually start from the hypothesis that man is a social being who develops in a healthy way by integrating himself into the society in a manner well adapted to its purpose.[58] The tendency is to regard society as healthier than its members.[59] An attempt is usually made to define what kind of society corresponds most appropriately to human needs, and to examine how the interaction between the society and its members can be most appropriately developed.[60] Man-

ifestations of illness in a society are regarded primarily as symptoms either of a perverse development in the relationship of the
society to its members or of a maladjustment of its members to
the society. Social policy in such a view is based on a theory of a
healthy and healing society to which individuals are taught to
adapt. One can also observe in sociology a tendency to understand
the manifestations of illness in different societies and groups as
"different symptoms of the same disease."[61]

Anthropological research presents the peculiar therapeutic methods of an Indian community as a concrete example both of the
communal nature of illness and of the community's therapeutic
encounter with it. The community, which lies in the countryside
of Guatemala (San Luis Jilotepeque) and consists of almost six
thousand members, tries to faithfully follow the traditions of its
rich Indian culture. One American researcher who has spent many
years studying the way the members of the community bear therapeutic responsibility for one another reports that the phenomenon
which in our culture is called nervous breakdown is called among
these Indians "magic fright."[62] It offers an escape to those who
for one reason or another cannot endure the pressure of the community's forms of life. When an attack occurs, one of the six
therapists (*curanderos*) of the village is called, some member of
the family serving as an intermediary. The patient is brought to
therapeutic interviews which are arranged weekly. The cost, which
must be paid in cash, is rather large, the intention being to make
the whole community financially responsible in the encounter
with illness. The therapist first carries on a diagnostic interview,
reviewing the patient's biography, his dreams, his interests, etc.
Then there usually follows "a releasing confession," after which
the therapist speaks to the patient "persuasively," gives the needed
medicines, and soon puts an end to the social isolation of the patient. At this moment one of the politico-religious leaders of the
community is called to participate in the therapy; he organizes
rituals, in which Christian saints often play a central role.[63] Many

magic stages in the treatment follow. Usually the treatment ends with the healing of the patient.

The central aim in this treatment seems to be to put the sick person in the center of a group which shows that the whole community desires the healing of the patient.[64] In all possible ways the attempt is made to get the patient out of social isolation. Even during the first stage of the treatment more than ten members of the community participate in the therapy, some of these being the patient's friends. The presence of the chief symbolizes the involvement of the whole tribe and at the same time urges the therapists to do their best.[65] When the treatment ends, a meal and festivities for all who have participated in the treatment is arranged in the beautifully decorated home of the patient. This meal signifies that the community welcomes the patient back to its life and work.

Although the sociopathological viewpoint can be found in various branches of research, the conclusions concerning the communal nature of illness to which it and the insights of Freud lead are only slowly coming to the attention of our culture. The conclusion that life together involves a process of integration or disintegration between individual and community organisms is still largely neglected. It is characteristic of the present situation that according to the suggestion of a committee of experts of the World Health Organization the term "social psychiatry" should be limited to those methods of treatment and preventative actions which seek to enable the individual to live a life that is useful in the framework of his social environment.[66] This emphasis means that even in social psychiatry the subject in illness is considered to be only the individual human organism.[67]

The tendency to dismiss the thought of the communal nature of illness—to dismiss the conception of the community organism as the subject of illness—is obviously deep-seated in our culture. In our analysis of the history of therapy, we have pointed out the tendency so to locate the reality of illness as to categorize it exclusively in mechanistic terms of cause and effect. The therapeutic encounter with illness in the death camp and in the camp of life speak clearly of the influence of this tendency in our culture.[68] The dismissal of the conception of the communal nature of illness is also manifest in how little, for example, the reality of concentration camps and the persecution of Jews has been studied and is studied among us. The way existing studies of concentration camps have been pursued gives further evidence of our tendency to ignore the communal character of illness.[69]

In the therapeutic encounter with illness insights drawn from the treatment of schizophrenia have thrown special light on the illness of the community organism. Those who deal with the schizophrenic, especially his doctor, realize that they are themselves a part of that split life which they are encountering. If, in encountering the one who is ill, they refuse to acknowledge their participation in the milieu of his illness, the worlds of the patient and of his therapist remain split.[70] The further one follows the patient into his split reality, the more obvious becomes the network of common guilt in which human beings are entangled.[71] The encounter with schizophrenia shows that the split life has emerged in a world where the communal nature of illness is denied; healing can be effected only through experiencing the illness as held in common. When schizophrenia is encountered as a common illness one discovers that there are also hidden in it possibilities of common healing.[72] Both becoming ill and healing are events in the whole community organism.[73]

As Martti Siirala has written of the encounter with the schizophrenic:

> . . . we see the sick person as a man in whose sickness and in whose total situation our inhumanity, our unlived life, our idolatry, and our blindness become crystallized; in the encounter this total situation is brought under judgment. The sick person is manifestly a prisoner under suspicion, hate, unfaith, and hopelessness, which qualities to a great extent remain hidden in us. He is as a stone crying out. Even though he is under the burden of all this, the Creator com-

pels the creature in him to cry out concerning his condition, if only we have ears to hear. . . (Mental illness is often thought of as a displacement, as a man "out of his mind," or "beside himself." Compare the German *Verrücktheit* and the French *Excedée*.) Being out of place means at the same time being a prisoner in the network common to all men. Not only the original cause of the anguish but also the continuation of it, and his increasing aloneness, are connected with our withholding our association from him. We protect ourselves from becoming entangled in his skein because what is revealed in him exposes our common guilt. . . We try to protect ourselves even against the anticipation that what we encounter here perhaps calls into question our whole reality, our faith, our conduct, our self-understanding. Here is perhaps the deepest reason for our strong need to isolate the anguish of illness and to keep it at a distance, beyond the reach of our ears.[74]

All we know is based upon what can be reaped from a particular slice of experience; it is from such a vantage point that men seek to take command of the whole world of experience. The dependability of such a vantage point is threatened by the thought of the communal nature of sickness and of healing. This threat appears to be one of the reasons for our difficulty in accepting a view of the community organism where sickness and health are shared. The experience of shared illness shatters this kind of "knowing," and clears the way for experiencing our existence as a reality lived in a prophetic situation.

What has been said of the individual human organism in the light of its pathology applies *mutatis mutandis* to the community as well:

There do not exist discrete, individual reactions of parts, as combinations of which the behavior of the organism can be understood. On the contrary, only knowledge of the whole organism leads us to understand the various reactions we observe in isolated parts. The response to a special stimulus depends upon the significance of that stimulus for the performance required of the whole organism at the moment of stimulation and is intelligible only from this point of view.[75]

One of the best-known contemporary research scholars on the subject of brain injuries states in his lectures on human nature in the light of psychopathology:

> Any attempt to determine what a normal social organization should be like is faced with the same epistemological difficulties as that of determining the characteristics of an organism. . . The study of a given social organization, like a study of an organism, has to be based upon the study of phenomena isolated by the analytic method; and we cannot proceed directly from these to a characterization of the whole which the social organization represents.[76]

The therapeutic encounter with illness seems to point clearly to the communal nature of illness and to the question of the very structure of our existence as a totality, as a community organism. But this is a question which easily disappears from our horizon.

6.   Healing Is Hidden in Illness

The case history of the illness of Elizabeth von Ritter draws a picture of the basic structure of our existence in which the forces that heal and the forces that destroy are inseparably entangled. Illness is hidden under health and healing under the encounter with illness. This is manifest in the way Elizabeth became ill and was restored to health. She became ill while her best qualities, the most powerful aspects of her being, were in the foreground; healing began when the hidden illness became overt.[77] When Elizabeth without sparing herself faithfully cared for the ill in her family, her way led to illness through this very activity. Freud asserted:

> He whose mind is occupied with the hundred different tasks of nursing which succeed each other continuously for weeks and months gets into the habit, on the one hand, of suppressing all signs of his own emotions, and on the other hand, his attention is soon turned away from his own impressions because he has neither the time nor the strength to do them justice.[78]

Healing is not to be found in so separating health and sickness that one strives to strengthen the qualities in himself which he considers healthy and to escape those he condemns as sick.

Freud continued his analysis of Elizabeth's life situation by describing it in the light of the illness which became manifest in it:

> While nursing her father, there occurred for the first time a hysterical symptom in the form of a pain in a definite location on the right thigh. . . It occurred in a moment during which the ideas of her duties towards her sick father came into conflict with the content of the erotic yearning which she then entertained. Under vivid self-reproach she decided in favor of the former and created for herself the hysterical pain. . . She repressed the erotic idea from her consciousness and changed the sum of the affect into somatic sensations of pain. . . Quite a similar conflict—of a highly moral significance and even better demonstrated by the analysis—repeated itself after years and led to the aggravation of the same pain. . . Again, it was an erotic idea which came into conflict with all her moral conceptions, for her affection for her brother-in-law, both during the life and after the death of her sister, and the thought that she should yearn just for this man, was very disagreeable to her. . . I must place reliance on the statement that the patient's affection for her brother-in-law, intensive as it was, was not *clearly known* to her except on certain rare occasions, and then only momentarily. If that were not so, she would have become conscious of the incompatibility between this desire and her moral ideas, and would have had to endure the same mental agonies which I saw her suffer after our analysis.[79]

This analysis emphasizes that therapy cannot be based on a separation between the forces which pervert life and those which restore it. We cannot simply define an ideal health to be sought and an illness to be avoided. Therapy cannot be based on "a knowledge of health and sickness." On the contrary, sickness manifests itself at that very point where there is a claim to know sickness and health. Elizabeth's consciousness was dominated by fixed conceptions of what was constructive and what destructive and she would not admit any elements to consciousness which could break these yardsticks, or measures of life. In this episode, the sources of Elizabeth's illness were in her categories of sickness and health; precisely these hindered her from letting the facts of her existence into her consciousness. Elizabeth did not become ill by repressing erotic ideas and obeying the voice of duty. The course of the events was not changed when her consciousness was dominated by another kind of knowledge of health and sickness or when she attempted to make an opposite decision by repressing the voice of duty. The decisive struggle between the forces which cause sickness and the forces that relieve it takes place on a deeper level.

Sickness occurs when the inseparable unity of constructive and destructive forces is denied and the attempt is made to avoid the conflicts of reality by applying one's own measures of life.[80] Elizabeth fell ill in just this kind of repression. She isolated one part of her being from her consciousness, as if it were a foreign body. She tried not to be conscious of it, although she did not succeed in this repression. Freud asked:

> How did it happen that such an intensively accentuated group of ideas could be kept so isolated? For generally the role of an idea in the association actually increases the size of its effect. This question can be answered if we take into account two facts: (i) that the hysterical pain originated simultaneously with the formation of these separate psychic groups, (ii) that the patient exerted great resistance against the attempt to bring about the association between the separate psychic groups and the rest of the content of consciousness, and when the union was, nevertheless, effected, she felt excessive psychic pain. Our conception of hysteria brings together these two factors with the fact of the splitting of consciousness, by asserting that (ii) contains the indication of the *motive* for the splitting of consciousness, while (i) shows the *mechanism* of the same. The motive was that of *defense* or the striving of the whole ego to get into harmony with this ideation group, and the mechanism was that of *conversion;* that is, instead of psychic pains which she spared herself, there appeared physical pains. A transformation was thus initiated, which resulted in a gain insofar as the patient had escaped an unbearable psychic state; to be sure, this gain was obtained at the cost of a psychic anomaly, a splitting of consciousness and physical suffering.[81]

Elizabeth's sickness manifested itself as a split in her consciousness, and her healing occurred as the isolated elements became integrated in a new way in her conscious being. When she dared to confront the distress which the encounter with the controversial reality caused in her conscious life, a healing formation of words took place. This, however, was painful and shattered her measures of life.

Elizabeth's attitude toward sickness and healing in her own being also shows that the healing structures of life are inseparably entangled with the factors that pervert life. As long as she was deaf to the voice of that illness which became manifest in her own organism, the healing structures could not break through; as long as she took the position that she as "healthy" took care of the "sick" without taking care of the patient in herself, she remained blind to the possibilities of healing hidden in the distortion and sickness of her being. The healing came from the encounter with illness. Healing structures began to grow just where her organism was most perverted.

7. Man's Urge for Death and Life

The peculiar mutual relationship between sickness and healing, between the tendencies which lead to death and those which lead to life, was also seen by Freud in the phenomenon that the sick person resists healing and strives by easily repeated attitudes to be fortified against healing. Freud dealt extensively with problems associated with this phenomenon, especially in *Beyond the Pleasure Principle* (*Jenseits des Lustprinzips*),[82] where he considered the functions of the death and life instincts. This theme became central in Freud's therapeutic work, and it is also so significant for this study that we have reason to examine it closely. In our examination we shall not confine ourselves to Freud's thoughts on the subject, but we shall deal with the theme as it is discussed in the therapeutic encounter with illness in general.

In the light of this theme life is seen as an unceasing struggle against illness. Times of health are times of "a cold war"; the struggle is the same but the methods are different. Health is realized as a conquering of illness: "One cannot derive the pathological from health, but one must try to follow the development of health from sickness."[83]

Sickness and death are realities which are present in all life. The human organism by its very nature is both sick and in the process of being healed, both dying and living. As the human body confines human existence in space, so sickness and death form its limits in time:

> Although psychoanalysts have been most seriously concerned with the interpretation of life's biological aspects, they have generally shared the common reluctance to face the positive meaning of death. This is particularly evident in their misunderstanding and neglect of Freud's own concept of the "death instinct." He defines its essence as the phenomenon: "the organism strives to safeguard its own individual path toward death. . . This leads to the paradox that the organism defends itself against the dangers which would allow it to reach the end through a short-cut." Although he considered this behavior as evidence of the power of instinct over the intellect, he lived up to his insight through sixteen years of fighting off his cancer of the jaw, working in self-fulfilment to his last day. His life illustrates poignantly the view of life as a defense against disease and as a creation of health.[84]

Behind Freud's thought on the death instinct is his theory of the character of human behavior. Man strives for pleasure (*Lust*) in such a way that the tensions which lead to displeasure (*Unlust*) are relieved or escaped, keeping the unpleasant tensions as powerless as possible.[85] Freud saw this leading principle in human behavior as closely associated with the urge he observed to reach stability and to sustain it.[86] In affirming the dominance of the "pleasure principle" in human behavior, he also acknowledged clear facts of experience which show that its dominance is not complete. One limitation is man's experience of reality. Reality threatens the existence of any organism which strives only for pleasure. The "reality principle" does not, however, change the basic structure of the behavior which strives for pleasure. It only compels the organism to postpone its goals and to endure pain on its way toward pleasure.

As another example of the failure of the pleasure principle to dominate, Freud examined neurotic pain. As the ego is forced to adapt itself to more and more complex systems, some part of the instinctual energy is repressed at each new stage.[87] Certain of these repressed instincts come into conflict with the consciously experienced instincts which at a given time dominate the whole ego. These repressed instincts are then in disunity or are isolated from the ego. They later tend to break in through some "side door" in order to seek and perhaps attain satisfaction for themselves. The ego experiences their success as pain, although under other circumstances it would be an experience of pleasure. This kind of neurotic agony is basically an experience of pleasure which cannot be felt as pleasure.

This phenomenon and other similar phenomena can still be explained in the light of the pleasure principle. However, the matter becomes more complex when those traumatic neuroses are studied in which external dangers are experienced as a threat to the whole human existence. According to Freud, the studies of dreams in traumatic neuroses made during the time of the First World War have shown that dreams bring the person repetitively before the situations of horror and fear which were the immediate cause of the neurosis. When the sick person awakes from his dream, he again experiences horror. While awake the victims of traumatic neurosis are not much concerned with their experiences of horror. The question then is: if these victims avoid thinking of their horrors in their waking moments, why is it that in their dreams, when they strive for the realization of their innermost wishes, they do not see pictures of their healthy past and of healing? Dreams associated with traumatic neurosis seem thus to say that there are also at work in man tendencies which strive toward self-destruction.[88]

After this Freud began to examine a phenomenon which he called "the compulsion to repeat," an urge to experience the same conflict repeatedly which could be observed in many instances.[89] Freud mentioned, for example, the child's wish to hear the same fairy tale again and again and the inclination to return to a life situation from which one has had to be separated. It is often possible to explain such repetitions of conflict in the light of the pleasure principle. Yet what can be said about the patient in therapy who compulsively reviews again and again events of the past? Here the pleasure principle seems to break down. The experiences the patient repeats again and again in therapy not only are painful to the ego at the time they are allowed to become conscious, but were painful when they were experienced in the first place. The experience differs from neurotic pain, where the question is of pleasure in one system and pain in another. These new experiences have never contributed toward pleasure, as neurotically painful experiences often have. They have always produced pain; yet they compulsively repeat themselves again and again.

One can also observe in the lives of many "normal" people compulsive repetition of behaviorial forms. In the life of one man, friendships are always broken in the same way; another man always has the same attitudes toward authority; the love life of another person is always realized in the same way. In such cases there is often talk of a fatalistic necessity or of being possessed, yet therapeutic experience with neurosis shows that man himself organizes his life as a reality which is realized through compulsively repeated forms of behavior. Behavior in cases of compulsive repetition seems to relate to the whole human ego in the form of a striving for pleasure.[90]

Some characteristics are out of place if man is seen as dominated only by the pleasure principle. These characteristics are manifested most clearly in the therapeutic encounter with illness where the patient exhibits a striving to return to those stages of development from which the human organism has been compelled to detach itself under the pressure of certain circumstances.[91]

Thus Freud gradually approached the thought that there is at work in the human organism an urge toward that inorganic stage from which the organism has grown. All life dies for inner reasons. Life is dying, returning toward the stage the organism was in before it began to live. It is not possible to explain from the viewpoint of life how the animate could come from the inanimate, but it is obvious that all living organisms have from the beginning struggled to return to that stage from which they grew. Initially it was easy for a living organism to die. Its span of life was evidently short and the behavior of the organism was mainly determined by its chemical structure. In the place of the dying organism there arose new living organisms. Gradually, as the organisms developed into more complex systems, the return to death became more difficult. The basic tendency of the organism, however, remained the same: to seek its own way back to its starting point.[92]

In the human organism the function of man's other instincts— for example, self-preservation—is organized according to the basic instinct, the "death urge" (*thanatos*):[93]

> They are component instincts whose function it is to assure that the organism shall follow its own path to death, and to ward off any possible ways of returning to inorganic existence other than those which are immanent in the organism itself. . . The organism wishes to die only in its own fashion. Thus these guardians of life, too, were originally the Myrmidons of death . . . The living organism struggles most energetically against events (dangers, in fact) which might help it to attain its life's aim rapidly—by a kind of short-circuit.[94]
> It may be difficult, too, for many of us to abandon the belief that there is an instinct towards perfection at work in human beings, which has brought them to their present high level of intellectual achievement and ethical sublimation and which may be expected to watch over their development into supermen. I have no faith, however, in the existence of any such internal instinct and I cannot see how this benevolent illusion is to be preserved.[95]

But what about the urge of the cells to form new organisms where life continues? And what about the sexual instincts which according to the experience gained by treatment of neurosis have so central a place in the behavior of human organisms? When Freud posed a question concerning the mutual relationship of the life and death instincts, he first pointed out that the external pressures which drive organisms to organize themselves in more and more complex forms do not meet all organisms in the same way. Many organisms remain in lower stages of development. Obviously, some organisms preserve a most primitive structure and need not seek a return to their original stage by such complicated means as the more highly developed organisms. For example, certain germ cells under favorable circumstances free themselves from the rest of the organism, become independent in their "behavior," and continue to repeat the rhythm of life which they have gained. These germ cells work against the death of the organism even if they do not achieve anything more than a prolongation of the span of life. The realization of this by the germ cells is possible only when they become united with a similar cell which is simultaneously dissimilar. The real instincts of their life are the sexual instincts which give protection to organisms when they are defenseless against influences of external reality, leading them to meet other germ cells and in various ways to protect their strivings. These life instincts work against those instincts in the ego which seek the way toward death.[96]

Freud, indeed, commented thus upon his own therapy in one account:

> It may be, however, that this belief in the internal necessity of dying is only another of those illusions which we have created *um die Schwere des Daseins zu ertragen* ("to bear the burden of existence," Schiller, *Die Braut von Messina*, I, 8). It is certainly not a primeval belief. The notion of "natural death" is quite foreign to primitive races; they attribute every death that occurs among them to the influence of an enemy or of an evil spirit.[97]

When Freud developed his thoughts further, he dismissed immediately the biological-morphological theory according to which living organisms consist of mortal and immortal elements. In the terms of this theory, the body (*soma*)—in the limited meaning of the word—is regarded as subject to a natural death, while potential immortality is hidden in the germ cells. These cells are even considered to have the possibility—under favorable conditions— of developing into a new individual, of adopting a new body.[98]

Freud indicated how his theory differed from such an understanding of the character of death. He rejected the idea that death is caused by certain circumstances and is not included in the structure of the organism itself. According to Freud, if death were a characteristic which the organism had acquired at a later stage, rather than in its very structure, one could not conceive of life itself as containing the death instinct. He pointed also to the theory of two opposite movements which can be seen in all organisms, the constructive (assimilatory) and the destructive (dissimilatory). In this theory Freud saw similarities to his own theory. He stated at the same time, however, that this kind of biological theory is not adequate to explain the behavior of human organisms in their complexity.

Freud found the best support for his own view in the theories of the structure of the conjugation of cells. On one hand, there is in each cell a tendency to discharge its chemical tensions (the death tendency); on the other hand, the conjugation of the individual cell with others increases the tensions in question and creates vital differences (the life tendency). The forming of multicellular organisms appears to be a means for the preservation of the life of individual cells. One cell helps another to maintain its life, and the community of cells is able to live even if some individual cells die. The conjugation of two cells has a life-preserving and rejuvenating influence for both of these cells, although as individuals they strive toward death. Freud saw in these phenomena similarities to those experiences gained in psychoanalysis on which his *libido* theory is based. "In this way the *libido* of our sexual instincts would coincide with the *eros* of the poets and philosophers which holds all living things together."[99]

8. Illness as a Stumbling Block

Among the different therapeutic schools of thought one can observe attempts either to integrate Freud's conceptions of *thanatos* and *eros* with a monistic interpretation of reality, or to dismiss them totally.[100] The "biological dualism" which Freud represents in the chain of reasoning presented above is conceived of as making an active therapy with a definite aim impossible. According to most therapeutic schools of thought, therapy has to be based on the presupposition that human nature is constructive.[101] Illness is seen, furthermore, as emerging from an encounter between the human organism and its environment.

Freud's biological dualism, which from the viewpoint of our theme is particularly significant, has been a stumbling block to an encounter with illness based on the natural sciences. The traditional conception of the human organism as a machine which functions according to physical and chemical laws dominates the biological explanations of the reality of sickness and death:

> Under the influence of mechanistic medicine this machine has been treated as if it could be kept indefinitely in running order, provided it were properly serviced and utilized within its specific limits of tolerance. Disease and death, in this view, are considered accidents capable of being warded off by the progress of science. To the extent psychology is admitted in this scheme of things, it plays the role of a mysterious form of energy added to temperature, electricity, and chemistry. In the form of "emotional tension" the psyche seemed to be capable of damaging the organism, and it was assumed that the "constitutionally weakest part" of the mechanism was specifically liable to psychological injury.[102]

Freud's biological dualism sought to overcome this view of the human organism as a machine which has no other purpose than to

operate ceaselessly. Freud's dualism was not absolute in the sense
that the life and death instincts were seen simply as opposite tendencies which eliminate each other. The life and death instincts are
in a unique way intertwined with each other. In some ways Freud's
rational pessimism colored his view so that destructive tendencies
obtain special emphasis.[103] His basic intention, however, was to
emphasize that every human organism becomes sick and dies in
its own unique way. Illness and death as human realities are unique
as are all things which happen to human organisms. The human
organism expresses itself in the form of its disease and death.[104]

This view makes it impossible in the encounter with illness to
treat man in his sickness only in mechanistic categories of cause
and effect. The functions of both the death and the life instincts
in the human organism are such that it becomes impossible to understand their character if they are separated from the individual
and from the situation where they are at work. The death and
life urges are not autonomous forces or self-regulating realities in
which certain causes mechanically effect certain results.[105] Every
human organism develops its own unique way of becoming sick
and of becoming well, of dying and of living.

If human life is examined as an interplay of mechanistically
viewed forces, the individual man disappears from view. One
closes his ears against the message which is to be heard in the encounter with illness. When the encounter with illness is based on
this kind of knowledge of health and illness, its goal becomes the
mobilization of the forces of health against the enemy, illness. The
main emphasis is on holding the illness within certain bounds.
Various psychological methods, antibiotic substances, X-rays, the
surgeon's knife, and the vaccines—all of which have their own
importance in their own place—are then mobilized against the
illness in such a way that one forgets that illness and death are
unavoidable. When vivisection became a fashion in the second
decade of our century, Bernard Shaw stated in his book *The Doctor's Dilemma*:

The people who are striving to make vivisection one of the watchwords of our civilization, are not doctors: they are the British public, all so afraid to die that they will cling frantically to any idol which promises to cure all their diseases, and crucify anyone who tells them that they must not only die when the time comes, but die like gentlemen. In their paroxysms of cowardice and selfishness they force the doctors to humor their foolish ignorance.[106]

In the midst of therapy louder and louder voices arise to warn our culture against ignoring the individual character of illness and healing:

Anxiety caused by the problems of personal existence and of society no longer needs to find a meaningful solution in terms of comedy and tragedy. Today more and more the technique is developed to make people insensitive to conflicts so that neither their own nor their neighbor's comfort will be disturbed. "Had tranquilizers been available in Robespierre's time the course of history might have been different" runs the caption under the scary portrait of this revolutionary which a pharmaceutical firm sends out as advertisement.[107]

Therapy which encounters man in illness holds open the prophetic perspective. When man's nature is only considered to follow laws and variances which have been observed in nonhuman realities as well as in man himself, the prophetic perspective is lost. The categories of cause and effect must be applied to the behavior of the human organism if a phenomenon is to be analyzed in isolation for a definite purpose. When man's behavior is examined in the full interplay of all the forces of his existence, when man is studied as a psychological reality, the categories of cause and effect are misleading.[108]

9. Therapy Leads to Prophetic Questions

From the viewpoint of our theme it is most important to pay attention to the general structure of Freud's line of thought. In following Freud's presentation one gets a strong impression that almost in spite of himself Freud wrote meditations on the tangled net of the death and life urges. Experiences in therapy brought him to a prophetic question. Again and again he attempted to escape it, but each time he returned to wrestle more seriously with the problem.

Even in the very beginning of his book *Beyond the Pleasure Principle,* Freud stated that he was ready to express his gratitude to any philosophical or psychological theory which could clarify the questions of the character of pleasure and pain which so urgently emerged in the therapeutic encounter with illness.[109] Freud could, however, see no help available from any source. As if against his own will the therapist had to move into almost inaccessible areas of human life.[110] This continuous encounter with inaccessible reality in therapy drove Freud to state that during his twenty-five years of psychoanalytic practice he had been forced to revise continually the goals and the techniques of his work.[111] These revisions led Freud to re-examine many conceptions which he had himself taken for granted.

These experiences led Freud to state in another connection that the message of illness conveyed by psychoanalysis would become a stumbling block for the whole world.[112] He feared that he was creating illusions "to bear the burden of existence," and he complained about the short-circuit solutions of some of his colleagues.[113] When he turned to his favorite science, biology, he stated that the whole conception of death melted away in the hands of the biologists.[114] In the same breath he said that biology after some decades might cast unexpected light on these problems. In anticipation of this light he turned, albeit hesitantly, to the world of mythology, and found there insights which encouraged him to go further in the direction he had already begun to take. Freud stated also that the tension between destructive and constructive forces encountered in therapy is such that one should not become embarrassed at the terminological difficulties to be met in describing it:

We must be patient and await fresh methods and occasions of research. We must be ready, too, to abandon a path that we have followed for a time, if it seems to be leading to no good end. Only believers, who demand that science shall be a substitute for the catechism they have given up, will blame an investigator for developing or even transforming his views. We may take comfort, too, for the slow advances of our scientific knowledge in the words of the poet: *Was man nicht erfliegen kann, muss man erhinken* ("What we cannot reach flying we must reach limping," *Die beiden Gulden* by Ruckert).[115]

What Scheler said of mankind in general in our time can be said specifically of Freud:

In the ten thousand years of human history ours is the first era in which man has become a problem to himself, in which he no longer knows what he is, and at the same time knows that he does not know it.[116]

The therapeutic encounter with illness has a vital inner pressure which leads to the situation we have called prophetic. In the encounter with illness one meets destructive and healing forces in such a way that they do not seem to fit into other categories of experience. It is one thing to seek answers to the questions of our existence in terms of the categories of good and evil, of truth and falsehood, of beauty and ugliness; it is quite a different thing to seek to understand our existence as a simultaneous process of becoming ill and of emerging from illness, as moving at the same time toward death and toward life. Our previous categories are not sufficient to encompass this understanding of reality. When reality is examined from the viewpoint of sickness and health, we observe a completely unique interplay of forces. Destructive and constructive forces appear in the therapeutic encounter with illness in such a way that their examination seems to presuppose a quite specific viewpoint. Reality as an interplay of these forces seems to open itself only in a prophetic perspective.

If this hypothesis is valid, the experiences of man's existence gained in the therapeutic encounter with illness have a central significance for prophecy. In therapeutic encounters the prophetic perspective opens or closes.

Chapter 4

Therapy and Prophecy

1. History as Therapy and Prophecy

"Luther is a patient of exceeding import for Christendom" (*en for Christenheden yderst vigtig Patient*).[1] These words of Kierkegaard have been chosen by the American psychoanalyst Erik Erikson as the starting point for his study of the sixteenth-century reformer, Martin Luther.[2] We see in his study, *Young Man Luther,* an expression of the same prophetic dimension of the therapeutic encounter with illness of which we have been writing. Accordingly we now turn to an examination of how prophecy is viewed by therapy.

In choosing these words of Kierkegaard as a starting point for his study, Erikson desires to emphasize that Luther experienced deeply the communal nature of illness and strove passionately to express both his sufferings and his urgent search for healing.[3] Luther's proclamation of the word was born in the midst of an encounter with illness.

We have already pointed out in many ways how the therapeutic encounter with illness leads us to view both individual and community life as a dramatic struggle between destroying and healing forces. When the encounter with illness is taken seriously, life is viewed from a perspective radically different from that in which the reality of illness and death is ignored. The interplay of forces in all that man experiences is now seen in a new order. His experience of life and death, of sickness and healing, brings him to a crisis in his understanding of good and evil, beauty and ugliness,

111

truth and falsehood. The story of Elizabeth von Ritter is a telling
example of the way man has to rewrite his life history if he sub-
mits himself to the anxiety which comes of facing the healing and
destroying forces of life. The encounter with both healing in sickness and life in dying opens such a new perspective that a new life
story must be written.

In the new story, former interpretations of experience break
down and the events of life find a new setting. Events of life which
have been repressed from conscious experience as meaningless become alive again and must be integrated in a new way. Time takes
on new content, and the periods of a life are connected with each
other by a thin red line of experienced crisis.[4] In the therapeutic
encounter with illness, out of the sufferings of the sick person
comes a unique "report on the sick": man's history in the light of
his illness. The time measured by man (*chronos*) becomes a time
which measures man (*kairos*).[5]

Erikson places himself in a position to listen to the Luther who,
as he was emerging from adolescence to adulthood, shared the
sickness of his time and sought healing in it. He calls this development the identity crisis.[6]

> Young patients (as well as extraordinary young people) make
> rather total demands on themselves and on their environment.
> They insist on daily confirming themselves and on being con-
> firmed either in their meaningful future or in their senseless past;
> in some absolute virtue or in a radical state of vice; in the growth
> of their uniqueness or in abysmal self-loss. . . . When suddenly
> confronted with such a conflicted young person the psychoanalyst
> may learn for the first time what facing a face, rather than facing
> a problem, really means, and I dare say, Dr. Staupitz, Martin's
> spiritual mentor, would know what I have in mind.[7]

In delving deeply into the life history of Luther, Erikson makes
use of the therapeutic principle that a man has to be heard from
within the history to which he belongs, and that history has to
be read "from a man's face," i.e., as it becomes flesh and blood in

a human being. Referring to the second part of the statement by Kierkegaard, ". . . of very great import for Christendom," Erikson makes the point: "This calls for an investigation of how the individual 'case' became an important and historic 'event,' but we clinicians have learned in recent years that we cannot lift a case of history out of history."[8]

Erikson asserts that psychoanalysis has followed the wrong lead when the life situations encountered in illness have been explained exclusively in terms of the earlier life situations of the individual in question. "Originology," which attempts to find for sickness one fixed "original cause" from the earliest period of life, blinds us to the fact that both the analyst and the patient are enmeshed in the community organism.[9] Erikson refers in this connection to the words of the historian Collingwood, "History is the life of mind itself which is not mind except so far as it both lives in the historical process and knows itself as so living."[10]

Erikson's work illustrates how the therapeutic encounter with illness breaks down the existing divisions of "research." These divisions are the consequence of seeing illness as a separate category of reality.[11] The subtitle of Erikson's book is "A Study in Psychoanalysis and History." He tries to show that not only the study and therapy of illness but also the history of the individual and the community become distorted if they are not in organic correspondence with each other. In relation to psychoanalysis, "unhistoricity" has led to indifference to whether the experiences and the theories of the encounter with illness have been conveyed to others—that is, to the prophetic function of therapy. Erikson points out that it is possible to see the psychoanalytic movement as having caused ethical sickness in many persons, even when it was concentrating on healing.[12] The brief history of psychoanalysis shows also how strongly various ideological movements have influenced the way psychoanalysis has formed its theories.[13]

Psychoanalysis has on occasion been one-sided in its interpretation of the ideological concerns of the youth growing from adolescence to adulthood. These concerns have often been interpreted as defense mechanisms, and have frequently been seen only as a reflection of the instinctual conflicts of the age.[14] As Erikson points out, however, a youth growing toward adulthood can confront the ideological concerns of his era so immediately and intensely that he may be said to be participating in the processes of history. During the developmental stage between puberty and adulthood, the content of tradition fuses with the new possibilities hidden in the growing human being and a new person may be born. Too little attention has been paid to the structure of the rhythm of generations, and to the working of ideologies in this rhythm: "What we have learned as pathologists must become part of an ecology of the mind before we can take full responsibility for the ideological implications of our knowledge."[15]

Obviously, it is when Erikson has Luther for his "patient" that he is driven to emphasize strongly that the forming of words takes place in the interplay of the forces at work in history as a whole. Luther's wrestling with the word is of such a nature that the expressions forced through his lips become meaningless if they are examined merely as "signals" of some crisis in his individual life. From the viewpoint of our theme, the emphasis Erikson places on "the ecology of the human mind" implies that therapy is a prophetic situation. In therapy, not only is the forming of words examined in its function as signal, but man is actually encountered as a historical being. In the forming of words man is viewed in the prophetic function where his integration into the history of mankind occurs. Human organisms are united with the community organism through their forming of words. It is at this point of integration with mankind that man becomes a man. The life of the community organism becomes history when its member organisms become human in their forming of words.

It is a telling coincidence that some years after the publication of Erikson's book, a Lutheran theologian, Joseph Sittler, produced a study on preaching which bears the title *The Ecology of Faith*.[16]

Ecology is defined as the science that deals with the mutual relationship between organisms and their environment. As I have reflected upon the many elements that constitute the situation to which Christian preaching is directed I have sought for an analogy big enough and rich enough to do justice to all the trees, and at the same time lure the mind to the forest. The facts of the biological and botanical world seem to supply such an analogy.[17]

To illustrate, Sittler describes a common landscape, a village located on the banks of a river that flows between high hills. Village life conforms to the seasonal changes from spring to autumn. The villagers know how high the spring floods will rise and they build their homes and shops above the flood line. There is also a natural balance in the hillside forests between the trees, the earth, and animal life. There is an ecological balance. Under the bark of the trees are millions of beetles which would destroy the trees if they could work undisturbed but which are in turn the prey of the birds. The balance, however, is disturbed when one tree falls to the soft ground, and the beetles underneath, protected from the birds, proliferate to the point where the balance between birds and beetles is destroyed. Tree after tree is attacked by beetles and dies, and the hillside erodes as the entire network of roots which has held the soft earth together loosens its grasp. When the spring rains come, the erosion of the hillside has completely transformed the landscape. The old rhythm of the life of the river has been broken by events which originated in the falling of a tree. The homes and shops are threatened by floods because some beetles hidden in a tree violated the ecological balance. Thus:

Every situation in which the Word of God is declared in preaching is a place and a moment on the riverbank; and the permeability of that time and place to the declared Word is bound up with the forests, the birds, the beetles, and the waters of history. From Incarnation to culture is a straight line, for the determination of God to embody his ultimate Word places man's relation to that Word inextricably in the web of historical circumstances. The Word is not naked, it is historically embodied.[18]

Hence both therapy and prophecy have been stirred to examine mankind as a community organism where separate events and experiences are bound together into a history by the forming of words.[19] When the nature of community as an organism is forgotten, the perspective of history narrows and the content of man's responsibility is comprehended in a limited way.[20] If life is lived exclusively in a community whose perspective is limited to its own space and time, then the content and meaning of history is determined solely by the interests of the community in question. Unity which is based only on contact and communication always has narrow limits. In such a community history becomes an element which splits life, for only when unity is experienced as communion can history become a healing force:

> The etiology[21] of neurosis implies a theory of history. History is information about the lived past, the living present and the future to be lived obtained in response to questions. It arises spontaneously and is communicated verbally and nonverbally. History is aftereffect; it is integrating organismal memory. History as therapy is the reconstruction and resolution of those factors that participated as etiology in producing neurosis. . .[22]

Healing is experienced as a new integration of history.

This experience of the significance of time in therapy is associated with the crisis our culture faces in understanding the categories of space and time. Paul Tillich, for example, points out that in various fields of study time and space are now seen in a new way as the basic elements of existence:

> Time and space belong together: We can measure time only by space and space only by time. Motion, the universal character of life, needs time and space. . . Time without direction is time under the full control of space. Therefore, it is the first victory of time that the process of life goes from birth to death, that growth and decay create a direction which cannot be reversed. The aged cannot become young again in the realm of life. Nevertheless, the predominance of space remains. The life process cannot be reversed, but it can be repeated. Each individual life repeats the law of birth and death, of growth and decay. The

direction of time is deprived of its power by the circular motion
of continuous repetition. The circle, this most expressive symbol
of the predominance of space, is not overcome in the realm of
life. In man the final victory of time is possible. Man is able to
act towards something beyond his death. He is able to have
history, and he is able to transcend even the tragic death of families and nations, thus breaking through the circle of repetition
towards something new. Because he is able to do so, he represents the potential victory of time, but not always the actual
victory.[23]

What Freud termed the "compulsion to repeat," an expression
of the death instinct, can be placed in a larger context. The compulsive return to previous life forms, there to stagnate, which has
been experienced in therapy as one of the basic obstacles to healing appears to be a phenomenon in the universal struggle between
the forces of space and time. It is from this viewpoint that the
most fruitful examination of Freud's attitude toward religion can
take place.

When Freud describes religion as an illusion or as a neurosis,
he does not mean that religion is only an illusion created by wishful thinking. Rather, according to Freud it is in religion that man
expresses the immortal desires of the human heart distorted by
repression.[24] These like all other desires of man are realized in a
perverted way. Man is sick even in his religion. Religion is a neurosis in which man seeks healing for his most difficult sickness.[25]
Religion means for Freud, to use an expression from Marx, "the
sigh of the oppressed creature, the heart of a heartless world."[26]

Tillich has also pointed out that the same struggle between the
forces of time and space can be seen in the growth and decay of
both religions and national ideologies. The religiosity which is
called pagan gives some limited area of space absolute priority
and worth. Its god being bound to a specific location, pagan religiosity is always polytheistic. The gods of different groups, nations, and areas are opposed to each other because the god of each
locality is by nature imperialistic. The forces of space lead un-
avoidably to a mutual destruction:

Modern nationalism is the actual form in which space is ruling over time, in which polytheism is a daily reality. Nobody can deny the tremendous creativity of national community. Nobody would be willing to deprive himself of the physical and psychological space which is his nation. . . But on the other hand, our generation has experienced again and again the most terrifying mutual animosity of the space-centered powers.[27]

Human existence under the predominance of space is tragic.[28]

Greek tragedy and philosophy knew about this. They knew that the Olympic gods were gods of space, one beside the other, one struggling with the other. . . Greek tragedy, philosophy, and art were wrestling with the tragic law of our spatial existence. They were seeking for an immovable being beyond the circle of genesis and decay, greatness and self-destruction, something beyond tragedy. But the power of space was overwhelming in Greek mind and existence. . . Even the logic of Aristotle is a spatial logic, unable to express the dynamic trend of time. There is no philosophy of history in Greek thought, and where history is dealt with it is considered as only a section of the long circular motion of the whole cosmos from birth to death, of one world replacing the other.[29]

What escape can there be from this world where space alone dominates? If one remains in the magic circle of the forces of space one has finally to attempt to break out of reality into the world of the mysterious where time and space lose their meaning.[30] Yet Tillich has pointed out that this, too, fails:

Mysticism is the most subtle form of the predominance of space. It is the most subtle form of denying history . . . therefore we can say that mysticism . . . is the most sublime form of polytheism. In the abyss of the Eternal One, of Atman-Brahman, of the Pure Nothing, of the Nirvana, or whatever the names of this nameless one may be, all individual gods and their spaces disappear. But they only disappear, and therefore they can return. They are not overcome in time and history.[31]

In the therapeutic encounter with illness which we have described, we have seen illness revealed as a world where individual and community organisms escape their real history. In illness the attempt is made both to confine the organism to a particular space which is measured by a certain fixed image of life, and to escape from that space because it stifles life. The sound of the voice of illness has led us to study the foundations of our attitudes toward history and time. Therapy uncovers both individual and community history and time as realities in which the forces of death and life, of destruction and healing, are in conflict with each other. Mankind reveals his illness in his interpretation of history. Both individual men and mankind in general are influenced in their choice of categories for interpreting history by a desire to repress from consciousness those anxiety-filled experiences and afflictions which do not fit their adopted world-view or their image of God. In sickness and in healing, however, history is experienced as a history of corruption and salvation. "For the therapist . . . a philosophy of history has to take the form of an eschatology, declaring the conditions under which redemption from the human neurosis is possible."[32]

This understanding of the role of history in sickness and healing has led Erikson, for example, to attempt to correlate psychoanalysis and the study of history. In assessing the damage which "unhistoricity" has done psychoanalysis, Erikson has emphasized that history cannot be left to the professional scholar or other such observer who classifies historical events as if he were himself outside the sick reality. Such an investigator rationalizes and idealizes the facts of our common history just as a sick person escapes his own factual history. In his study of Luther, Erikson has illustrated this muting of history by reference to the treatises on theology which either ignore those crises in Luther's life which were attended by illness, or explain them by some fixed theological scheme.[33] In such treatises, word-formation and life history are so far divorced that Luther and the student remain in the enchanted land of ideology:[34]

> To relegate Luther to a shadowy greatness at the turbulent conclusion of the Age of Faith does not help us see what his life really stands for. To put it in his own words: "I did not learn my theology all at once, but I had to search deeper for it, where my

temptations took me! *Vivendo, immo moriendo et damnando fit theologus, non intelligendo, legendo, aut speculando* ('A theologian is born by living, nay dying, and by damning himself, not by thinking, reading, or speculating')." Not to understand this message under the pretense of not wanting to make the great man too human—although he represented himself as human with relish and gusto—only means to protect ourselves from taking our chances with the *tentationes* of our day, as he did with his. Historical analysis should help us to study further our own immediate tasks, instead of hiding them in a leader's greatness.[35]

We began our study by examining the dilemma with which the afflictions of our own time confront Christian preaching and community life. We continued with a sketch of the message of our illness as heard in a therapeutic encounter with these afflictions. Both our examination of the history of the encounter with illness and our examination of the nature of our present illness seemed to say that our attitude toward history is one of the central issues in the dilemma.[36] The manner in which we encounter our illness determines whether our history will lead toward perdition or salvation. The struggle between sickness and healing takes place as we face history.[37]

An unhistoric interpretation of history has deeply influenced the development of both therapy and prophecy in our culture.[38] Our description of the common history of therapy and prophecy has shown that an overemphasis on naturalism has imprisoned therapy and prophecy in fixed ideologies. In contrast, the therapeutic encounter with illness has required us to examine reality from the viewpoint of the history of salvation. Therapy has thus led to the basic questions of prophecy.

It is obvious that the prophetic perspective disappears from view when the struggle between the forces which corrupt and those which heal is disregarded.

Tillich points out that outside the Jewish-Christian tradition only in Persia did a historic interpretation of reality develop as a dualistic religion.[39] The Persian dualism, albeit a factor in the common history of therapy and prophecy, shows that the human mind cannot endure absolute dualism: "A complete dualism would destroy the unity of the human mind, would be a metaphysical schizophrenia."[40] All authentic interpretation of history, whether the history of individuals or of communities, discerns a pattern of struggle between two dynamic principles, the destructive and the constructive. In one form or another, all such interpretation is messianic: there is an expectation of a divine being who is to solve the conflict of world history by bringing about a victory of the good, a resurrection of true humanity, a judgment of individuals, and a destruction of evil. Persian religion, however, forfeits its historical character, as Tillich points out, through its doctrine of a dual creation involving an absolute contradiction between good and evil: there is evil present in reality which cannot be overcome by history, and the history therefore cannot become a history of salvation. There are, in these terms, elements of reality which must be destroyed. In Persian religion, God cannot become absolute Lord of history because he is not the creator of all things.

The influence of this kind of dualism upon the development of therapy and prophecy is manifest in those persecutions which have formed essential elements in the dilemma we have tried to analyze.[41] The persecution of the mentally ill and the persecution of the Jewish people shared a common motivation. The reality of illness is a scandal because in it we see ourselves as part of the universal community organism. In the same way, the Jewish prophetic tradition is a stumbling block, for to assert that the God of all reality speaks through man is to break the bondage of human word-formation to space and time. In writing of Jeremiah, Buber says:

> The contact between godhead and manhood in his view is not bound up with the rite but with the *word*. The rite is a work of man and it is accepted or rejected by God, according to the feelings of the men performing it; whereas the word comes again and again from heaven as something new and makes its abode within man.[42]

His words here simply mean this, that God does not attach

decisive importance to "religion." Other gods are dependent
on a house, an altar, sacrificial worship, because without these
things they have no existence, their whole nature consisting only
of what the creatures give them; whereas "the living God and
eternal king" . . . is not dependent upon any of these things,
since He is. He desires no religion, He desires a human people,
men living together, the makers of decision vindicating their
right to those thirsting for justice, the strong having pity on the
weak, men associating with men.[43]

According to this view, God wants his people to stand in the prophetic situation where he speaks.[44] Men love the words and images
of their own hearts, but God shows through his prophets that there
exists a reality of truth which requires that they listen. God's grace
is costly. He does not surrender himself to the people to be adored
as a helper conformed to their desires. His word is at work in the
midst of human words; yet from the viewpoint of those human
words his word is almost powerless. He does not make his word
believable, but he lets man choose between difficult truth and an
easy lie. God does not show his power in order to corroborate his
word, nor does he place even a particle of his omnipotence on the
scales of the human heart.[45] False prophets deify their own unconscious. The authentic prophetic word asks man to listen:

> But no word of Jeremiah is simply personal; his sufferings,
> though he does not know it, are transparent into the sufferings
> of Israel—not the sufferings of one generation, still less of this
> corrupt generation, but the sufferings of the eternal people. . .
> In general those who tend to distinguish precisely in Scripture
> between the collective and the individual "I" are mistaken.
> The "I" of the individual remains transparent into the "I" of
> the community . . . the "I" of Jeremiah passes over directly into
> the "I" of the people. . . He really bears the people within him-
> self. The contradiction that destroys the people resides in his
> very self. . . The sufferings which he bears because of Israel
> he bears for Israel.[46]

In this solidarity of suffering man experiences God's universal
presence which destroys all local gods. Tillich says the same thing:

> Jewish prophetism . . . must be considered as the real birth-place of a universal historical consciousness in world history. . . The idea of one creation which is essentially good and one mankind which, although fallen from its original innocence and unity, shall be blessed through the history of the elected nation— all these give a framework for an entirely historical interpretation of history, as developed in the Old Testament: the call of Abraham implying the demand to separate himself from the spatial gods of his father's house and to follow the God of time and the future who is the God of all nations; the exodus from Egypt as the fundamental event, the center of history, for Israel; the covenant between God and his nation; the prophetic threat that God might punish and destroy even his elected nation; the promise that the exiled remnants will become the bearers of the world-historical aims of God, that a messianic king out of David's seed will arise, that in the last day, in the day of Yahweh, all his enemies will be overcome and Jerusalem will become the center of true adoration, justice, and peace, peace even in nature. This is the Old Testament interpretation of history. Here it is obvious that God reveals himself not only *in* history but also *through* history as a whole. The gods of space are overcome; history has a beginning, a center, and an end.[47]

It is noteworthy that both therapy's encounter with illness and its conception of history as the battlefield of destroying and healing forces have flourished on Jewish soil. From the Jewish people, whose body has been bloodied and scarred in the very midst of Christianity, sounds forth the harsh message of the split in the unity of therapy and prophecy. Here voices call us to seek healing by examining our common history. In this examination Christianity must confess the communal nature of illness.

If prophecy puts itself above history it becomes, in Luther's expression, "a theology of glory" (*theologia gloriae*) which leads to an arbitrary interpretation of events from a fixed position to which the observer has isolated himself. The theology of prophecy must be a theology of cross and shame (*theologia crucis*) where the reality of history can overcome that use of words which seeks to escape the judgment of history.[48] This is relevant also to the establishment of Christian community. If unity is not sought in a prophetic spirit, Christian ecumenicity becomes utopian and

"polytheistic," a melting pot of various local gods. The key problem of Christian preaching and the formation of community is
constantly its relationship with the Jewish prophetic tradition.[49]
The voice of this tradition echoes powerfully in our time precisely
in the midst of the therapeutic encounter with illness.

2. The Prophetic Word in a Sick World

> In Luther's new *theologia crucis,* the Christian, like Christ
> himself, must voluntarily submit to crucifixion by the Devil.
> "To take up the cross is voluntarily to take upon oneself and
> bear the hate of the Devil, of the world, of the flesh, of sin, of
> death." And as Christ harrowed hell by offering Himself for
> hell whole and entire so "God leads down to hell those whom
> He predestines to heaven, and makes alive by slaying." Hence
> it is one of the signs of predestination to heaven not merely "to
> be resigned in very deed to hell" but even to "desire to be lost
> and damned." It would be hard to find a clearer illustration of
> the actuality and effective power of that death instinct which
> Freud postulated and which the non-Freudian world has ridiculed.
> For hell, Luther said, is not a place, but is the experience of
> death and Luther's devil is ultimately personified death. Luther's
> new *theologia crucis* rejects the traditional Aristotelian-Thomistic
> goal of actualizing the potentialities of life as *amor concupis-
> centiae,* and calls us to experience hell on earth, to experience life
> on earth as ruled by the death instinct, and to die to such a
> death-in-life, in the hope of a more joyful resurrection.[50]

So writes Norman Brown, a student of psychoanalyisis who sees
in Luther, as Erikson does, a man of prophetic stature for Western
history, a man who paved the way for that therapeutic encounter
with illness in which Freud is the central figure.[51] Both see in
Luther one who wrestled to reconcile death and life, wrath and
love.

Erikson examines Luther as a man who sought his identity, who
tried to be himself, who tried to mean what he said and to say
what he meant in his innermost being in circumstances where the
identity crisis of a maturing man became especially difficult.[52]

The starting point of Erikson's presentation is a graphic description of Luther as he entered life's third decade casting himself to the floor in the choir of the monastery at Erfurt and crying as if possessed, "It isn't me."[53] Even though this description is probably inaccurate historically, Erikson is properly expressing Luther's inner state at that time. The attack occurred during the reading of the passage in the Gospel of Mark which tells of a father's bringing Christ his son, who is possessed by a dumb spirit (Mark 9:17-29). Luther's desperate cry evinced a serious identity crisis. The young man felt that he had to protest against a voice which called him possessed. He protested against what he was not, in order to force himself into what he was and what he would be. These struggles led Luther to stand firm before the powers of the world and to say a decade later, "To act against one's conscience is neither safe nor honorable."[54]

Luther's teachers in Erfurt, who primarily followed Occam's thought, emphasized that reality is a battlefield between forces of life (*generatio*) and death (*corruptio*); only God stands outside these forces. When he so wills, God can bring the dead to life or put an end to life. The urgent question for Luther thus became: "How is it possible to find out when and on what ground God justifies and accepts man?"

Luther experienced, on the one hand, the domination of the life urge over man: "Since, without our flesh, we would not exist, and could not operate, neither could we exist without the forces of the flesh (*sine vitiis carnis*), nor operate without them."[55] Erikson states that Luther is in this respect Freud's forerunner, since Luther was emphasizing that the *libido* rules every moment of man's life.[56]

On the other hand, Luther experienced in himself a conscious and inextinguishable hatred of God, and a desire to die. When Luther sought his identity in this conflict he had to confront the three principal solutions offered by his time. Dismissing the solution of the mystics,[57] he sought his real self primarily in the thought categories created by the main streams of medieval philosophy, realism and nominalism.

When we examined the history of the encounter with illness we stated that both one-sidedly naturalistic and one-sidedly theological tendencies have led men to avoid illness as a psychological reality. Erikson's analysis of Luther shows that both nominalism (the naturalistic tendency) and realism (the theological tendency) were approaches rejected in his search for healing for the illness of his own being and his own time. Luther did not find "the man of good conscience," his real identity, in the conclusions of either: realism[58] offered a false security, nominalism[59] left the conscience insecure.

Furthermore, the Thomistic synthesis appeared to Luther as a conception which hindered the conscience from encountering anxiety in a healing way. Erikson calls the identity offered by Thomism "rational." In his theological system, Thomas Aquinas combined the reality of things and the study of natural forces in a way which made it possible to experience identity by penetrating, with the help of reason, to that order which lies beneath the world of experience. God is the sovereign first truth (*prima veritas*) who reveals himself in his creation and his goodness can be read in the order creation reveals. Man's nature lies in his ability to understand God's message which appears as divine order. Although man can never fully comprehend God's will, he is able to differentiate between good and evil sufficiently to base the life of his conscience on a reasonableness which is guided by revelation:

> St. Thomas reserves a place for active and reasonable conjecture where before there was room for only faith and hope. In his philosophy man as a contemplator acquires a new identity, that of a "theorist" . . . verified by a divine order perceived by reason. . .[60]

Thomas Aquinas thus created a synthesis of classical and Christian thought:

Luther's question was, however, whether, in this synthesis, problems of conscience are not drawn into the sphere of reason, rather
than reason being incorporated into faith.[61]

Luther realized that the ceremonies whose purpose was to express
the divine order had become separated from conscience; they had
become means used by the ruling classes to avoid bearing the
burden of the afflictions of the time. These ceremonies salved the
pain of plague, syphilis, the threat of the Turks, and the struggles
for power between ecclesiastical and secular authorities. The afflictions were not encountered but escaped. The Thomistic synthesis did not offer an identity to the afflicted. It gave identity
primarily to the spiritual and secular intelligentsia and aristocracy.

Humanism has been previously described as a movement which
prepared the ground for a right hearing of the voice of illness. In
his analysis of the Renaissance Erikson states that the golden age
of humanism did not bring the solution it had promised, a good
conscience.[62] He says of the Renaissance:

> This view again anchors the human identity in the hierarchy
> of organs and functions of the human body, especially insofar as
> the body serves (or is) the mind. Renaissance sensuality tried to
> make the body an intuitive and disciplined tool of reality; it did
> not permit the body to be sickened with sinfulness, nor the mind
> to be chained to a dogma; it insisted on a full interplay between
> man's senses and intuitions and the world of appearances, facts,
> and laws. . . We need no proof of (God's) identity nor of ours
> as long as an essential part of our equipment and a segment of
> His world continue to confirm each other.[63]

The Renaissance meant, according to Erikson, a rebellion of the
self against the fact that the church had begun to achieve dominance by misusing men's inclination to live by negative conscience.
Negative conscience means a life attitude in which man bases his
identity on his awareness of sinfulness. In Luther's time, according to Erikson, the church promised deliverance from bodily desires if man resigned himself to his negative conscience, giving to
the Church the authority to punish and reward, the authority

which defined the content of the consciousness of sin. The Renaissance tried to deliver man from this negative conscience.[64] The attempt led to ideological utopianism:

> Who could deny that man possesses as it were almost the same genius as the Author of the Heavens? And who could deny that man could somehow also make the heavens, could he only obtain the instruments and the heavenly material?
>
> —FICINO

With the bad conscience of such a godlike man both theology and psychiatry have wrestled. The Renaissance created new possibilities of identity for those who in art or in science could examine the fruits of their labor and be encouraged that their strivings were justified. However, one has to remember, as Erikson points out, that Ficino who in his youth addressed his pupils as "Beloved in Plato" in his forties became a monk, Pico della Mirandola died as a devotee of Savonarola, and Leonardo and Michelangelo, in giving expression to the rebellion of the masculine self actually examined and expressed its defeat:

> Surely existential despair has never been represented more starkly than in the Sistine man facing eternal damnation, nor essential human tragedy with more dignity than in Michelangelo's Pieta. One must review the other Madonnas of the Renaissance (della Robbia's, del Sarto's, Raphael's) who are shown with the boy Jesus making a gay and determined effort to stand on his own feet and to reach out for the world, to appreciate Michelangelo's unrealistic and unhistorical sculpture—an eternally young mother holding on her lap the sacrificial corpse of her grown and aged son. . . Renaissance man contained within himself the same contradictions which are the burden of all mortals.[65]

Erikson describes Luther's lifework as an inner struggle to overcome the negative conscience against which the Renaissance was also in rebellion. Luther, however, sought the good conscience via the perverted conscience, and did not bypass the latter as did the Renaissance man.[66] Luther's weapons in the struggle were the same as those of Renaissance humanism: a return to the original texts, a definite anthropomorphism (although in a christocentric form) and a concentration on using the special gifts hidden in one's own being—in Luther's case, verbal expression:

> Forced to speak his mind in public, he realized the rich spectrum of his verbal expression, and gained the courage of his conflicted personality. . . Nervous symptoms harassed his preaching; before, during and after sermons he was on occasion attacked by dizziness. The popular term for dizziness is *Schwindel,* a word which has a significant double meaning, for it is also used for the fraudulent acts of an imposter. And one of his typical nightmares was that he was facing a congregation, and God would not send him a *Konzept.* But I think the psychiatrist misjudges his man when he thinks that endogenous sickness alone could have kept Luther from becoming a well-balanced (*ausgeglichen*) creature when his preaching brought him success. After all, he was not a Lutheran; or, as he said himself, he was a mighty bad one. On the frontier of conscience, the dirty work never stops, the lying old words are never done with, and the new purities remain forever dimmed. . . To Luther the inspired voice, the voice that means it, the voice that really communicates in person, became a new kind of sacrament. . . He obviously felt himself to be the evangelical giver of a substance which years of suffering had made his to give; an all-embracing verbal generosity developed in him, so that he did not wish to compete with professional talkers, but to speak to the people so that the least could understand him: "You must preach," he said, "as a mother suckles her child."[67]

Thus Luther experienced the forming of words as an essential element in the search for a good conscience. A perverted word creates a perverted conscience, and a negative conscience stifles the living word.

From the viewpoint of our theme it is essential that we come to terms with Luther's insistence that the prophetic word cannot be proclaimed independently of an encounter with the illness experienced by the proclaimer of the word and by his time. The living word has to be sought beneath the words which have become distorted in the sick life situation. The theological study of the word and its proclamation are to be done through the sickness of the one who is involved and of his time. Theology has to remain, as we stated above, a theology of the cross. If one proclaims the word in such a way as to put oneself outside the common illness, if theology thus becomes a theology of glory, the word becomes petrified into an ideology and preaching becomes propaganda.

When Erikson, speaking of Luther as a proclaimer of the word, states that Luther was not Lutheran, he touches a sore point in the present Protestant proclaiming of the word. Tillich points out the same thing when he writes:

> "Word of God" is an ambiguous term. It is often used in the sense of the written word of the Bible. But no biblical word is the word of God for us so long as we have to give up our historical reality in order to understand it. The "Word of God" is every reality through which the ultimate power breaks into our present reality, a person (e.g., the Christ), a thing (e.g., a sacramental object), a written text (e.g., the Bible), a spoken word (e.g., a sermon). It is the greatest emergency of the Protestant churches of today that they have not yet found a way of preaching in which contemporaneity and self-transcending power are united. The ecclesiastical, and to a great extent the biblical, terminology is removed from the reality of our historical situation. If it is used, nevertheless, with the attitude of priestly arrogance which repeats the biblical word and leaves it to the listeners to be grasped by it or not, it certainly ceases to be the "Word of God" and is rightly ignored by Protestant people. And the minister who feels himself to be a martyr of "divine" frustration—and even becomes ecstatic about this frustration—is guilty of a lack of contemporaneity.[68]

Luther's prophetic struggle for a good conscience is especially interesting from the therapeutic point of view because Luther expresses so boldly the illness both of his own being and of his own time. Luther found healing precisely in his sickness, not in escape from it; in a continuous encounter with the controversies of his own being he found a new identity. Erikson is right in saying penetration into the world of the Psalms was decisive for Luther, for in the prayers of the psalmists man's heart opens for God to see his entire being with all its conflicts and sickness:

> The theology as well as the psychology of Luther's passivity is that of man in the *state of prayer*, a state in which he fully means what he can say only to God: *Tibi soli peccavi*, I have sinned, not in relation to any person or institution, but in relation only to God, to *my* God. . . Luther made a virtue of what his superiors had considered a vice in him, namely, the determined search for the rock bottom of his sinfulness: only thus, he says, can man judge himself as God would: *conformis deo est et verax et justus*.[69]

In the Psalms Luther learned to listen to the gospel: God's righteousness is in us, in that faith which is working in us.

Luther found the Christ hidden in the very reality of life; identity was found in the Christ:

> This paradoxical foolishness and weakness of God became a theological absolute for Luther: there is not a word in the Bible, he exclaimed, which is *extra crucem* . . . Luther spoke here in passionate terms very different from those of medieval adoration. He spoke of a man who was unique in all creation, yet lives in each man; and who is dying *in* everyone even as he died *for* everyone . . . What he had tried, so desperately and for so long, to counteract and overcome he now accepted as his divine gift—the sense of utter abandonment, *sicut jam damnatus*, as if already in hell . . . The Passion is all that man can know of God: his conflicts, duly faced, are all that he can know of himself. The last judgment is the always present self-judgment. Christ did not live and die in order to make man poorer in the fear of his judgment, but in order to make him abundant today: *nam judicia sunt ipsae passiones Christi quae in nobis abundant* . . . The artist closest to Luther in spirit was Dürer, who etched his own face into Christ's countenance.[70]

According to Erikson, Luther encountered God's reality in the afflictions and conflicts of his own life.[71] God did not mean for him a goal to be reached; rather God was for him a way which begins in the very midst of those afflictions which man encounters: *via dei est, qua nos ambulare facit.*[72]

Norman Brown follows Erikson in many theological judgments. "Protestantism was born in the temple of the devil, and it found God again in extremest alienation from God."[73] An experience of omnipresent evil not submissive to man's control drove Luther to proclaim in his theology that the devil is the god and ruler of this world. Luther could say, "It is an article of faith that the devil is *princeps mundi, deus huius seculi.*" Yet this article of faith is also based on experience: "The devil is the Lord of the world . . . I have had some experience of it: but no one will believe me until he experiences it, too. . . . The world is the devil and the devil is the world."[74] Man meets the ruling grasp of the devil both in his vices and virtues: "Outside of Christ, death and sin are our masters and the devil our god and sovereign, there can be no power and might, no wit or understanding whereby we could make ourselves fit for, or could even strive after, righteousness and life, but on the contrary we must remain blind and captive, slaves of sin and the devil. . . . The devil lets his own do many good works, pray, fast, build churches . . . and behave as if he were quite holy and pious." The devil also guides man's reason and conscience: "Conscience is a beast and bad devil. . . . conscience stands in the cruel service of the devil; the man must learn to find consolation even against his own conscience."[75]

In Luther's conception of the power of the devil, Brown finds the same emphasis as in Freud's view of the death urge. In his proclamation of the word and in his theology, Luther has provided insight into the power of death in life at the same time as he has awakened the hope of another kind of life, an eternal life:

> The positive features in Luther are his diabolism and his eschatology. Actually the diabolism and the eschatology are two sides of the same coin. It would be physically impossible for Luther to recognize the Devil's dominion over this world . . . without the faith that the Devil's dominion is doomed and that the history of man on earth will end in the kingdom of God . . . Hence the decadence of Protestantism may be measured by the decline of diabolism and eschatology. Theologies . . . . which lack

a real sense of the Devil lack Luther's capacity for critical de-
tachment from the world . . . Already Luther had discerned that
the worst of the new assaults of the Devil were those in which
"one does not know whether God is the devil or the devil God."
Decadent Protestantism does not have this problem.[76]

The denial of the devil leads also to a pale eschatology. If it is
proclaimed that man can free himself from the power of the devil
by some decision of faith, there is no need for an eschatological
message concerning a time when the kingdom of grace becomes
visible. In that situation the Christian pretends to be outside the
sick situation, and is not in a struggle with the devil, sin, and
death:

> Neo-orthodox Protestant theology, with its triumphant vindi-
> cation of the demonic and its failure to produce an eschatology,
> is not hope, and it is in danger of becoming, like so much in
> the modern world, merely the love of death. Luther's ethic, like
> the ethic of primitive Christianity, is an interim ethic looking
> forward to the speedy abolition of its own premises. If neo-
> orthodox Christianity cannot foresee the kingdom of Christ on
> earth, it consigns this earth to the eternal dominion of Satan.[77]

Brown's discussion of this hopelessness is carried on within the
framework of a study of Luther's position in regard to the rising
capitalism of his time. Brown uses the difficult term "capitalism"
to describe the "magic hope" which treats money as the decisive
factor in any solution to the human predicament. His argument is
rooted in Luther's passionate claim that the kingdom of Satan was
being realized in the rising capitalism. To be sure, studies of Luther have since tended to disregard this claim as the sentimental
outburst of a man whose economic thinking was primitive.[78] Yet
it has been to the detriment of Protestantism, according to Brown,
that Luther's claim that a satanic power is hidden in capitalism
has not been recognized as a realistic appraisal of the facts of life.
In Brown's view, one source of Luther's theology of the cross is
to be found in his experience of the demonic power of the rising
capitalism. Brown quotes Luther:

> Usury lives securely and rages as if he were god and lord in all lands.
>
> There is therefore no worse enemy of mankind on earth, next to the devil, than the covetous man and the usurer, for he wishes to become god over all men.
>
> Money is the word of the devil, through which he creates all things.

Thus to capitalism is ascribed the same aim as the devil: it tries to become the prince of this world. In Brown's judgment, Luther sees the kingdom of Satan gaining strength in burgeoning capitalism; indeed, the structure of the kingdom of Satan is capitalistic: we are the property of the devil.[79]

Brown lays stress upon the fact that Luther, although he saw the world under the devil's power, consciously surrendered himself to be crucified by the devil when he went from the monastery into the world. Luther believed that thus he was following Christ, who willingly chose the cross: "To take up the cross means freely to take upon oneself and bear the hate of the devil, of the world, of the flesh, of sins, and of death. . . . It is not necessary for you, like monks and hermits, to take up a special cross: remain with people and in your calling (*Beruf*); there the devil and the world will lay cross enough upon you." This view, an expression of the power of the death urge, was possible because of the hope of Christ's second coming which would end the power of death in life and make grace visible. When this historical eschatology began to weaken in Protestantism, Brown continues, belief in the power of death and the devil began to pale. Lutheran ethics began to speak of existing order as the order of God:

> With the elimination of the devil secular callings can be celebrated as simply appointed from God . . . From the standpoint of the original Protestant theology, the deification of capitalism and of the calling is the deification of the devil, or at least an utter confusion between God and the devil. From the psychoanalytical point of view if the devil is death, and if capitalism is the devil, then modern Protestantism's alliance with capitalism means its complete surrender to the death instinct.

Brown states that it is not accidental that Paul Tillich, who as a theologian has argued strongly for a clarification of the character of the demonic, has also made a vigorous attempt to separate Protestantism from its alliance with capitalism. Yet the eschatology of Protestant theology is so weak, Brown contends, that it is only employed in making diagnoses. It does not heal; it does not have the power to exorcise.[80]

Brown concludes his presentation of Luther by pointing out that the relation between psychoanalysis and religion cannot be solved in terms of the alternatives Freud provides: science and wishful thinking. Both psychoanalysis and religion are required to say that reality is not what it seems to be, and psychoanalysis must state that the reality which is revealed in religion is the same as that which comes to light in psychoanalysis. Psychoanalysis and religion represent stages in the return of repressed elements to consciousness, and both are realized within the sickness of mankind. To take seriously the insight that the history of mankind is a history of neurosis means that both psychoanalysis and religion share in the neurotic situation.[81] This means, furthermore, that seeds of healing germinate in the sickness itself; healing is experienced as a breakdown of the prevailing consciousness and as the increased anxiety of neurosis.

According to Brown, the profoundest psychological insight of Lutheran Protestantism is the unmasking and rejection of man's traditional manner of achieving salvation by sublimation. This it did by its doctrine of original sin. Furthermore, Brown continues, psychoanalysis must say that Luther was more consistent than Freud in the way he rejected all attempts to become spiritual by overcoming the body. This Protestant criticism of sublimation meant that *eros* refused to be realized by sublimation. Holy life means holy dying.

> Luther's vision of the dominion of death in life is correlative to his eschatological hope in the transformation of life on earth, and the transformation of the human body—the resurrection of

the body . . . Luther's eschatology challenges psychoanalysis to formulate the condition under which the dominion of death and anality could be abolished. Current psychoanalysis has no utopia; current neo-orthodox Protestantism has no eschatology. This defect cripples both of them as allies of the life instinct in that war against the death instinct which is human history; both are crippled in their capacity to cast out demons. Competition between the two to produce an eschatology for the twentieth century is the way to serve the life instinct and bring hope to destructed humanity.[82]

In the foregoing it has not been our intention to examine critically the studies of Erikson and Brown. Only some of their views have been emphasized. What has been presented shows, however, that the common problems of therapy and prophecy appear in both the therapeutic process and the study of therapy. In prophecy and therapy the same basic problems of life are encountered, and these problems are a part of human existence itself. Therapy cannot evade the challenge of prophecy, and prophecy cannot evade the test of therapy. Every individual and community function is both prophetic and therapeutic. Every man uses words which are either diabolic or reconciling, corruptive or healing, and the character of his word formation is decisively dependent upon how he encounters the reality of illness. When the therapeutic function is perverted, prophecy also becomes false, and vice versa. In the way that we as individuals encounter our illness and in the way we use words to reconcile our split being, we make a choice between real and fictitious healing and between true and false prophecy. In every man there is both the physician and the illness, the minister and the unreconciled conscience. The extent to which these are integrated in individuals depends upon how therapy and prophecy are realized in medicine and the ministry which represent them.

We have thus seen how significant for therapy is a study of the problems of prophecy. Yet prophecy has been even slower to examine the significance of therapeutic experience and study for Christianity than therapy to take account of prophecy. One of the best-known encyclopedias of religion, *Die Religion in Geschichte und Gegenwart,* corroborates this view:

> From the positions of theology today it is hardly possible to define satisfactorily the relationship between the theological and psychological doctrine of man. The theological doctrine of man either considers itself to be absolute and has hence to deny all correspondence between them regardless of all the similarities in the form of thoughts and expressions, or it names thematically some separate sections where one possibly can agree, leaving the questions of principle unsolved.[83]

In the article in which the significance of psychotherapy for theology is examined, it is further stated that psychology is without significance for a theology which considers the message of the church to be independent of the world of human knowledge. The article claims that this conception of theology dominates the present theological situation:

> Barth does not at all refer to a psychological doctrine of man, nor to the medical doctrine of man which has grown in such close relationship with it; Thurneysen on his part directly and radically dismisses the ability of psychology to understand and interpret the human personality. Psychology must refrain from all metaphysics and limit itself to an acceptance of the established facts of natural sciences which give more information about man; a real knowledge of man can grow from the biblical revelation.[84]

This survey article continues by stating that psychological and psychotherapeutic research is frequently acknowledged to have at best a merely practical importance for the preacher. It is well for the clergyman to know enough of psychology to be aware of the pattern of his listeners' psychic life; he should be able to draw the line between normal and abnormal mental life, and between a "pastoral problem" and a "psychiatric case." Any direct correspondence between psychology and preaching remains dubious, although psychological knowledge can show its significance indirectly. To the degree that it enriches an understanding of man's existence and of human experience it can also have an impact on the proclamation, even if it is not a determining factor.[85]

The picture which the encyclopedia article gives of the present relation between theology and therapy is in many respects all too accurate. Yet the article fails to reflect accurately the process of a deeper encounter with sickness now taking place in other segments of the life of Christianity. In the daily life of the church, in Christian preaching, and in the establishment of community, there is a great controversy between prevailing theological positions and the actual experience of proclamation and parish life.

In the encounter with the reality of illness, prevailing theological positions are coming under criticism. This phenomenon can be seen especially in America where various church bodies have made deliberate attempts to create an organic correspondence between therapy and prophecy. This movement has especially influenced the training of clergymen, so that seminarians are now given therapeutic experience as a part of their training. Added importance has been ascribed in the theological curriculum to both clinical training and the psychological sciences. In some theological faculties a chair of psychiatry has been established.[86] There is, furthermore, an increase in psychological testing of candidates for the ministry.[87] These are first steps in promoting a dialogue between therapy and prophecy although they still represent a rather small section in the total work of American churches and theological seminaries.[88]

The aims of this movement are firmly established and already its influence is spreading to discussions about the theological foundations of the training of ministers.[89] In the notes to this volume we have mentioned the studies of three universities—Protestant, Roman Catholic, and Jewish—engaged in examining the contribution of clergymen to mental health. The "Harvard Report" is of special interest from the point of view of our theme because it is an expression of the major crisis in the theology of the training of the clergy.

The Harvard Report provides illustrations of the problems which arise in theological discussions when prophecy is examined from the viewpoint of therapy. Although the concrete recommendations of the report do not include anything crucial for our theme, the structure of the presentation is significant. The starting point of the report is the assertion that the Chrisian proclamation of the word and formation of community in itself participates in the sickness to which the prophetic word is proclaimed and within which healing of life is sought for the community. This starting point represents a radical rejection of the view ascribed above to the encyclopedia *Die Religion in Geschichte und Gegenwart* in its article on the relation between theology and psychotherapy.

Perhaps the deepest expression of the present crisis in theology and preaching is contained in the prison letters of Dietrich Bonhoeffer. Bonhoeffer speaks of the "positivist-doctrine of revelation" (*Offenbarungspositivismus*) as a desperate attempt to preserve a theological position which has become untenable.[90] He also writes:

> The time when men could be told everything by means of words, whether theological or simply pious, is over . . . We are proceeding towards a time of no religion at all . . . Our whole nineteen-hundred-year-old Christian preaching and theology rests upon the "religious premise" of man. What we call Christianity has always been a pattern—perhaps a true pattern—of religion. But if one day it becomes apparent that this *a priori* "premise" simply does not exist, but was an historical and temporary form of human self-expression . . . what does that mean for "Christianity"? . . . How can Christ become the Lord even of those with no religion? . . . what is a religionless Christianity? . . . How do we speak of God without religion . . .? . . . I often ask myself why a Christian instinct frequently draws me more to the religionless than to the religious, by which I mean not with any intention of evangelizing them, but rather, I might almost say, in "brotherhood." . . . Religious people speak of God when human perception is (often just from laziness) at an end, or human resources fail: it is really always the *Deus ex machina* they call to their aid, either for the so-called solving of insoluble problems or as support in human failure—always, that is to say,

helping out human weakness or on the borders of human existence. . . . I should like to speak of God not on the borders of
life but at its centre . . . On the borders it seems to me better
to hold our peace and leave the problem unsolved. Belief in the
Resurrection is not the solution of the problem of death. The
"beyond" of God is not the beyond of our perceptive faculties.
The transcendence of theory based on perception has nothing to
do with the transcendence of God. God is the "beyond" in the
midst of our life.[91]

What we have written contains no solution to the way the word
of reconciliation should be proclaimed in the sick world. The
theological solutions now available are of no value, but resources
are nevertheless available to indicate the direction in which we
must go.

The first requirement is that Christian prophecy be challenged
to acknowledge its participation in our culture's common formation of words. This emphasis is especially clear in Bonhoeffer's
insistence that theology radically revise the method of its studies
of the prophetic function. The Harvard Report draws too much
attention to what should be studied and not enough to method.
The report also elicits criticism in that the issue of the study of
languages and the study of semantics is too easily overlooked. If
the living, reconciling word can break through only by shattering
the perversion of words, and if that word is stifled by the split
life, as we have attempted to show, then "the oppressive loquacity"
of our performance of the prophetic function cannot be healed
without a penetration into the deepest problems of perversion and
restoration in the use of words. Words are not formed outside the
reality of illness. It may be that the current philosophical analysis
of language is performing a service theology has neglected. Brown
writes:

> If psychoanalysis is carried to the logical conclusion that
> language is neurotic, it can join hands with the twentieth century
> school of linguistic analysis—a depth analysis of language—
> inspired by that man with a real genius for the psychopathology

of language, Wittgenstein. He said, "Philosophy is a battle against the bewitchment (*Verhexung*) of our intelligence by means of language.[92]

It is difficult to hold on to the prophetic word. It shatters the words and the life forms which have seized us in our unfaith and hopelessness. The prophetic word is not our own. Having experienced the power of the revealed word an apostle of Christ wrote, "And we have the prophetic word made more sure. You will do well to pay attention to this as to a lamp shining in a dark place, until the day dawns and the morning star rises in your hearts. First of all you must understand this, that no prophecy of scripture is a matter of one's own interpretation" (II Peter 1:19-20).

Epilogue

"Surely our diseases he did bear."
—Isaiah 53:4*

We began with a description of one physician's attempt to find ways of healing by examining a concentration camp in order to lay bare the illness of the whole community organism. To conclude, we present a selection from the letters of a theologian who was himself a victim of a concentration camp.[93] In these letters Dietrich Bonhoeffer often meditates on the meaning for our sick generation of that prophecy from which the quotation at the head of our epilogue is taken. The gospel's witness concerning the fulfillment of that prophecy in Christ was for Bonhoeffer the evidence of a new healing organism, the body of Christ.

*   *   *

"We should find God in what we do know, not in what we don't; not in outstanding problems, but in those we have already solved. This is true not only for the relation between Christianity and science, but also for wider human problems such as guilt, suffering and death. It is possible nowadays to find answers to these problems which leave God right out of the picture. It just isn't true to say that Christianity alone has the answers. In fact the Christian answers are no more conclusive or compelling than any of the others. Once more, God cannot be used as a stop-gap. We must not wait until we are at the end of our tether: he must be

---

*The Holy Scriptures: According to the Masoretic Text (Philadelphia: Jewish Pub. Soc. of Am., 1937), p. 544.

found at the centre of life . . . The ground for this lies in the revelation of God in Christ. Christ is the centre of life, and in no sense did he come to answer our unsolved problems."

•   •   •

"Unlike the other oriental religions the faith of the Old Testament is not a religion of salvation. Christianity, it is true, has always been regarded as a religion of salvation. But isn't this a cardinal error, which divorces Christ from the Old Testament and interprets him in the light of the myths of salvation? Of course it could be urged that under Egyptian and later, Babylonian influence, the idea of salvation became just as prominent in the Old Testament—e.g., Deutero-Isaiah. The answer is, the Old Testament speaks of *historical* redemption, i.e., redemption on this side of death, whereas the myths of salvation are concerned to offer men deliverance from death. Israel is redeemed out of Egypt in order to live before God on earth. The salvation myths deny history in the interests of an eternity after death. . . . The difference between the Christian hope of resurrection and a mythological hope is that the Christian hope sends a man back to his life on earth in a wholly new way which is even more sharply defined than it is in the Old Testament.

"The Christian, unlike the devotees of the salvation myths, does not need a last refuge in the eternal from earthly tasks and difficulties. But like Christ himself ('My God, My God, why hast thou forsaken me') he must drink the earthly cup to the lees, and only in his doing that is the crucified and risen Lord with him, and he crucified and risen with Christ. This world must not be prematurely written off. In this the Old and New Testaments are at one. Myths of salvation arise from human experiences of the boundary situation. Christ takes hold of a man in the centre of his life."

"God is teaching us that we must live as men who can get along without him. The God who is with us is the God who forsakes us (Mark 15:34). . . . Before God and with him we live without God. God allows himself to be edged out of the world and on to the cross. God is weak and powerless in the world, and that is exactly the way, the only way, in which he can be with us and help us. . . .

"This is the decisive difference between Christianity and all religions. Man's religiosity makes him look in his distress to the power of God in the world; he uses God as a *Deus ex machina*. The Bible, however, directs him to the powerlessness and suffering of God; only a suffering God can help."

*　　*　　*

"Jesus asked in Gethsemane, 'Could ye not watch with me one hour?' That is the exact opposite of what the religious man expects from God. Man is challenged to participate in the sufferings of God at the hands of a godless world.

"He must therefore plunge himself into the life of a godless world . . . He must live a 'worldly' life and so participate in the suffering of God. He *may* live a worldly life as one emancipated from all false religions and obligations. To be a Christian does not mean to be religious in a particular way . . . but to be a man. It is not some religious act which makes a Christian what he is, but participation in the suffering of God in the life of the world."

*　　*　　*

". . . not only action, but also suffering is a way to freedom. The deliverance consists in placing our cause unreservedly in the hands of God. Whether our deeds are wrought in faith or not depends on our realization that suffering is the extension of action and the perfection of freedom."

*　　*　　*

"Death is the supreme festival on the road to freedom."

Notes

CHAPTER 1. THE REALITY OF ILLNESS AND THE AMBIGUITY OF WORDS

1. *Our Illness*

1. This description is based on private discussions and information presented by J. W. R. Thompson, M.D., the founder of *l'Eau Vive*, who now teaches at Albert Einstein Medical College in New York, New York.

2. *The Problem*

2. F. S. C. Northrop, *The Logic of the Sciences and the Humanities* (New York: Macmillan, 1948), pp. 1-18.

3. *Ibid.*, pp. 22 ff.

4. *Ibid.*, p. 17, "One must begin not with the facts nor with . . . deductive reasoning nor with a hypothesis but with the problem and the problematic situation, because at the beginning of inquiry this is all that one has . . . It is the problem and its characteristics as revealed by analysis which guides one first to the relevant facts and then, once the relevant facts are known, to the relevant hypothesis."

5. Aarne Siirala, "The Meaning of Illness," *Journal of Religion and Health*, I, No. 2 (Jan., 1962), 157, "It is quite obvious . . . that the fact of illness—and especially of the illness of mind or of the spirit—has always been a stumbling block in Western culture. Only quite sporadically has the relevance and meaning of illness been seen. Western thinking on the nature of man is almost untouched by the fact of mental illness. What the German philosopher Simmel says seems to be true: 'It is embarrassing how little the pain of mankind is reflected in its philosophy.' "

6. In the paper "The Meaning of Health," delivered before the New York Society for Clinical Psychiatry, January, 1960, Paul Tillich described the view of man which has developed during recent decades in medicine, especially in psychiatry, as "multidimensional." According to this view, the being of man does not consist of layers—body, soul and spirit—which can be studied separately. Man is a multidimensional unity. In each dimension all other dimensions are potentially or actually present. When the physical dimension dominates, health is the adequate functioning of all

the particular parts of man; when the chemical dimension dominates, health is a balance of chemical substances and processes in a living organism; when the biological dimension dominates, health is a balance of the whole organism with its total environment, etc. The encounter with illness has to take place in all these dimensions. The hurt finger requires surgical or chemical help, the physically healthy neurotic requires psychotherapeutic help, etc. This encounter has to be seen as an interaction between the different approaches in the different dimensions. If one dimension alone predominates, the result of the therapy will be "an unhealthy health." Tillich points out, for example, that the present drug fad has meant a profound problem for our culture. With drugs and tranquilizers it is possible to remove some of the tensions of the human organism and of the human mind, which perhaps have an important positive function: "If it is possible to determine the self-altering as well as the self-preserving life processes in a living being from the dimension of chemism, what does this mean for the dimensions of the psychological, the spiritual and the historical? In answering this, one must realize that even if we imagined the total determination of individuals on this basis as possible, the question would remain: what about the chemism of those who determine the chemical composition of others?" Tillich concludes his paper by stating that the multidimensional view of man leads to a new interaction between medicine and theology: "Only a medicine which denies the non-biological dimensions of life in their significance for the biological dimension (including its physical and chemical conditions) must come into conflict with theology. But an understanding of the differences as well as the mutual within-each-otherness of the dimensions can remove the conflict and create an intensive collaboration of helpers in all dimensions of health and healing."

7. Gotthard Booth, "Health from the Standpoint of the Physician," in Paul B. Maves (ed.), *The Church and Mental Health* (New York: Scribner, 1953), pp. 3 ff., states that this crisis has been influenced especially by developments in the natural sciences. The mechanistic view of illness and health has been based on the determinist world-view, created by (among other things) the physics of the nineteenth century. The physics of our century has broken the image of a mechanistic world which does not have any purpose in itself and in which man learns gradually how to take command and organize: "The discoveries of Planck and Einstein revealed that the so-called laws of classical physics are really statistical generalizations or statements of probability, that there is no determinism, and that what had been considered inanimate nature is not the passive object it had appeared to be. When refined laboratory techniques were applied to the relationship between organism and environment the concept of man as the autonomous engineer of the world had to be abandoned even more completely" (pp. 11-12).

8. David Rapaport has edited a series of essays, *Organization and Pathology of Thought* (New York: Columbia Univ., 1951), which contains, critically analyzed, the most important studies in this field.

9. Gregory Zilboorg and George Henry, *History of Medical Psychology* (New York: Norton, 1941), hereafter referred to as *HMP*, pp. 53 ff., describe this process as a crisis—a confrontation especially with the Aristotelian tradition of thought. Aristotle, who laid the foundation for psychological research, established categories which left no place for listening to the voice of illness in the study of the character of human behavior. "Reason is creative and is independent of man or matter, it is immortal. It cannot be attacked by any illness because of its immaterial and immortal nature. This orientation should be carefully noted; it was destined to play, overtly or covertly, a decisive role in the whole history of psychiatry, for it definitely leads, as it actually did lead Aristotle, to the conclusion that only man and his so-called lower souls can become ill. This point of view . . . must insist that every mental illness is a physical, organic illness" (p. 55).

10. In the literature of psychology there is no standard classification of the different schools of thought. In her large study on psychoanalysis, Munroe classifies different schools of thought according to their attitude toward the libido-theory of Sigmund Freud; Ruth L. Munroe, *Schools of Psychoanalytic Thought: An Exposition, Critique, and Attempt at Integration* (New York: Dryden, 1955). The "Freudians" are, e.g., Anna Freud, Heinz Hartman, Abram Kardiner, Erik Erikson, Sandor Ferenczi, Melanie Klein, Karl Abraham, Wilhelm Reich. The most prominent representatives of the other group, the non-libido schools, are Alfred Adler, Karen Horney, Erich Fromm, and Harry Stack Sullivan. The third group consists of those analysts who cannot be classified on this basis and who have been less important in developing clinical methods. In this group are mentioned, e.g., Carl G. Jung and Otto Rank.

The *American Handbook of Psychiatry*, edited by Silvano Arieti (New York: Basic Books, 1959), uses the classification "psychotherapeutic and psychoanalytic." In the psychotherapeutic group are the psychobiological, the existential, and the psychodramatic schools of thought. The psychoanalytic group consists of the classical school of thought, the movement which analyzes the interpersonal and cultural factors (Sullivan), the school of thought which emphasizes the holistic view of man (Horney) and "other psychoanalytic schools" (Jung, Adler, Rank).

In the present study no comprehensive survey of the different therapeutic movements is given nor is an analysis of the content of the views of different schools attempted. The material has been chosen and will be analyzed exclusively from the point of view of our theme.

11. G. Bally, "Das Diagnosenproblem in der Psychotherapie," *Der Nervenarzt*, II Heft (1959), pp. 483 ff.; Martti Siirala, *Die Schizophrenie des*

Einzelnen und der Allgemeinheit (Göttingen: Vandenhoeck & Ruprecht, 1961), pp. 43 ff.

3. *Human Existence in the Light of Illness*

12. Ernest Jones, *The Theory of Symbolism* ("Papers on Psychoanalysis"; London, 1948), pp. 85 ff.; Munroe, *op. cit.,* pp. 10 ff.

13. Suzanne K. Langer, *Philosophy in a New Key* (New York: New American Library, 1958), pp. 53-54; Paul Tillich, *Theology of Culture* (New York: Oxford Univ., 1959), hereafter referred to as *TC,* pp. 54-60, and *Systematic Theology* (Chicago: Univ. of Chicago, 1951), I, 122-25. *Systematic Theology* copyright (Vol. I, 1951; Vol. II, 1957) by The University of Chicago.

14. This discussion is doubtless a sign of a confusion in the forming of words in the different fields of research. Our culture no longer has a common language, such as was in use in the Middle Ages when the scholastics functioned as a linguistic "clearing house." Immanuel Kant with his philosophy of categories sought to lay the foundations for such a language, but there is now almost a vacuum. Current discussions concerning the symbolic character of words are signs of an attempt to clarify the research on the structure of the forming of words. In this respect logical empiricism is obviously raising an important voice in our culture. Tillich, *TC,* p. 53, states: "We have no such clearing house, and this is the one point at which we might be in sympathy with the present-day so-called logical positivists or symbolic logicians generally. They at least try to produce a clearing house. The only criticism is that this clearing house is a very small room, perhaps only a corner of a house, and not a real house. It excludes most of life." Langer, *op. cit.,* pp. 30 ff., presents a bibliography and a short review of the literature which deals with these problems.

15. Booth, "Conditions of Medical Responsibility," *Review of Religion,* XIII (March, 1949), 244, writes: "Psychoanalysis has made it clear that the psychological constellations are based only to a limited extent on the reasoning processes of the conscious mind. To a much larger extent our psychological reactions are caused by the symbolic quality of the situation, regardless of our conscious awareness." Booth points out that Freud did not pay attention to the positive meaning of symbolic processes because he was to a great extent a prisoner of the mechanistic science of his time. Freud considered the unconscious world primarily a threat to the conscious life. The goal of therapy became to enlarge the area of consciousness so that the threatening reality could not split human existence. Booth continues, "The procedure of classical psychoanalysis followed the theory used in physical therapies: the patient was sick because a bad childhood situation had conditioned bad functioning, he was to be cured by subjecting him to the good, rational conditions of the analyzed psychiatrist." It was Jung, Booth states,

who first developed a theory according to which the symbolic functions of the unconscious life are expressions of the basic structure of human existence: "The symbolic order of the unconscious cannot be understood as part of a chain of causes and effects, but represents the permanent forms within which the fleeting events of life and the changing experiences of the conscious mind take place."

16. See Langer, *op. cit.*, p. 22, who mentions that Whitehead calls this dichotomy of subject and object (*res cogitans—res extensa*) "the bifurcation of nature." This dichotomy has dominated Western thinking since Descartes. It has resulted in categories such as subject versus object, inner experience versus outer world, individual reality versus general truth. Medard Boss, "Daseinsanalytische Bemerkungen zu Freuds Vorstellung des Unbewussten," *Zeitschrift für Psychosomatische Medizin,* Jan.-Mar., 1961, p. 134, says that behind such a scientific view of man are three "philosophical dogmas": (1) there exists an outer world which is independent of man; (2) only that which is real, which is concrete, can be conceptually grasped; (3) man is a thing, a concrete being with a certain place in the world of things, in concrete reality.

17. This "protest" is not directed against an "objectivating" perception and research as such. Our concern is with the place of objectivating research in the context of life. Cf. Paul E. Pruyser, "Phenomenology, Existential Psychology and Psychoanalytic Ego Psychology," *The Christian Scholar,* XXXXIV (1961), 59, "For the outside world and its sensory qualities is not only there in all its intricacy and splendor but has also healing powers, as every occupational therapist knows. And knowing and perceiving need not to be contrasts. . ."

18. Booth, "Conditions of Medical Responsibility," *op. cit.,* pp. 248-49. Immediately before the passage quoted Booth presents an African legend from L. Frobenius, *Kulturgeschichte Afrikas* (Zurich, 1933) which shows the depths of the crisis in a culture when its symbolic structure breaks. The legend tells of the fall of the kingdom of Kash. In that kingdom life for a long time had been successfully linked to the movements and the revolutions of stars. The priests watched them carefully, and whenever a certain constellation appeared the reigning king was sacrificed and a new king chosen. Thus the renewal of life was anchored in the order of the cosmos. Finally, however, this harmony was broken by the attitude of an individual, one man who did not want to die according to the laws of the universe, because he had fallen in love. He considered life with the woman he loved more significant than the order of the kingdom. He hypnotized the priests by telling them fairy tales and was able to distract their attention at a decisive moment from the movement of the stars. Thus the life of the king was saved and the life of the kingdom flourished in all respects for many generations. Finally, however, this aroused the greed of the neighboring tribes and they destroyed Kash. Booth presents this as an example of his

view that the dynamics of the world of symbols are of great importance in
the reality of illness.

19. In this case one has to consider the forming of words in human organisms as predominantly "unrealistic," because only some parts of the vocabulary of man can be seen as identical with reality. In his book *The
Tyranny of Words* (New York: Harcourt, Brace, 1938), pp. 46-56,
Stuart Chase analyzes the behavior of his cat Hobie Baker in the following
way: "Hobie can never learn to talk. He can learn to respond to my talk,
as he responds to other signs . . . He can utter cries indicating pain, pleasure, excitement . . . But he cannot master words and language. This in
some respects is fortunate for Hobie, for he will not suffer from hallucinations provoked by bad language. He will remain a realist all his life . . .
Generally speaking, animals tend to learn cumulatively through experience.
The old elephant is the wisest of the herd. This selective process does not
always operate in the case of human beings. The old are sometimes wise,
but more often they are stuffed above the average with superstitions, mis-
conceptions and irrational dogmas. One may hazard the guess that erroneous identifications in human beings are pickled and preserved in words,
and so not subject to the constant check of the environment, as in the
case of cats and elephants . . . Most children do not long maintain Hobie
Baker's realistic appraisal of the environment. Verbal identifications and
confused abstractions begin at a tender age . . . Language is no more than
crudely acquired before children begin to suffer from it, and to misinter-
pret the world by reason of it." Langer, *PNK*, p. 41, is right in replying
to this that one should first inquire whether the structure of human existence does not differ basically from that of the cat before thus character-
izing the language of man as unrealistic.

20. Martin Buber, "The William Alanson White Memorial Lectures,"
Psychiatry, XX (1957), No. 2, hereafter referred to as *WAWL*, 101, analyzes the character of artistic expression when he tries to show that structurally the relationship of man to the world of things is totally different
from that of the animals: "Art is neither the impression of natural objectivity nor the expression of spiritual subjectivity, but it is the
work and witness of the relation between the *substantia humana* and the
substantia rerum; it is the realm of 'between' which has become a form."

21. Cf. Booth, "The Role of Physical Form in Psychodynamics," hereafter
referred to as *RFP, Psychoanalysis and the Psychoanalytical Review*, XLVII,
51-62. Buber emphasizes that when we speak of man's special character as
a symbolizing being we say that man is a spiritual being for whom reality
becomes a world. The animal has only an environment—that realm of life
which it experiences with its senses. Its life is conditioned by the special
environmental conditions in which it lives. The animal gathers from its
environment those elements which are necessary from the point of view of
its own needs and creates its own life space. The image formed by the

animal of its life space is totally dependent on its experiences of its life space. The animal is inside its perceptions as a nut is inside its shell; it does not have a world in the proper sense of the word. The word world here means a reality which transcends subjective experience. Only man experiences reality as a world, as a totality, as a unity. For man, reality is more than an object for examination, the experience of which determines his life image as in the case of animals. Reality becomes for man, or in any case can become for man, a unity, a whole.

Cf. Buber, *WAWL*, p. 99, "Rather is this the peculiarity of human life, that . . . a being has arisen from the whole, endowed and entitled to detach the whole from himself as a world and to make it an opposite to himself, instead of cutting out with his senses the part he needs from it, as all other beings do, and being content with that. This endowment and this entitlement of man produce, out of the whole, the being of the world . . ."

22. Harold Kelman, "Communing and Relating," *American Journal of Psychotherapy*, XIV, No. 1 (1960), 82.

23. Those psychologies which say that needs build the basic dynamics in the human organism consider the forming of words to be the last stage in the developmental process: man begins to form words in order to have means to satisfy his more developed needs when the dynamics of the needs have reached a certain stage. This theory, however, meets difficulties when it faces the factual structure of the forming of words in human organisms. However the needs of man may then be defined, an essential part of the forming of words is meaningless from the point of view of the needs of man. If the basic structure of human existence is to satisfy needs inherent in the human organism, in a manner well adapted to their purpose, why is language not more appropriate to the needs than it actually is? Langer, *PNK*, pp. 39-40, states that studies concerning the use of words, studies based on a biogenetic view, have led to the conclusion that man is using words in a manner which, from the biological point of view, is undeveloped and inappropriate. The titles of such studies are themselves suggestive: *Short Introduction to the History of Human Stupidity* (Pitkin), *l'Homme Stupide* (Richet), *The Tyranny of Words* (Chase).

24. Kurt Goldstein, *Human Nature in the Light of Psychopathology* (Cambridge: Harvard Univ., 1951), refers to extensive material from research on speech disturbances resulting from brain injuries that shows language to be more than a means. "Speech automatisms may be designated as 'tools,' but it is false to consider language in general as a mere tool . . . It is not merely a superficial means of communication, not a simple naming of objects through words; it represents a particular way of building up the world . . ." (pp. 82-83). Goldstein goes on to say that his studies have shown that formation of words by the human organism has the character of an abstraction. There is no satisfactory explanation for disturbances in speech if the human organism is considered to consist of different kind of

needs which seek release from their inherent tension (p. 140). The tendency to release tension seems to be a characteristic phenomenon of pathological life: "The tendency to discharge any tension whatsoever is a characteristic expression of a defective organism, of disease. It is the only means the sick organism has to actualize itself, even in an imperfect way" (p. 141). As a counterbalance to these sick tendencies the organism as a whole attempts to actualize itself through a forming of words which result in an abstract language characteristic only of the human organism.

25. Helen Keller, *The Story of My Life* (Garden City, New York: Doubleday and Co., 1921), pp. 23-24; cf. Langer, *op. cit.,* p. 63.

26. Langer, *op. cit.,* pp. 63, 107.

27. Cf. Dietrich Bonhoeffer, *Sanctorum Communio* (Munich: Chr. Kaiser-Verlag, 1954), hereafter referred to as *SC,* p. 66, "What in community is a means toward an end (advertisement)is in communion a symbol. This corresponds with the difference between the goal-directed action of the former and the action of self-realization in the latter."

4.   *Symbolic and Diabolic Forming of Words*

28. Jurgen Ruesch, "Psychotherapy and Communication," in J. L. Moreno (ed.), *Progress in Psychotherapy* (London and New York: Grune & Stratton, 1956-58), I, 180 ff., says that psychopathology has grown out of a methodological study of disturbances in verbal communication. These disturbances are experienced in all common human life but they are generally ignored in favor of a very superficial "verbal" confrontation. In fact, everyday life itself is always altogether "psychotherapy." We are influencing one another in a destructive or constructive way whenever we use words, whenever we speak and listen. According to Ruesch, therapeutic research should not submit to a pathological use of words: "In science there is today a growing awareness that the observer's way of reporting and the limitations in language distort our thinking." Cf. Boss, "Wirkungsweise und Indikation der Psychotherapie," *Schweiz. Med. Wochenschrift,* No. 6 (1957), p. 11: "All the actions of the so-called physical medicine are also psychotherapeutic in function, whether the physician is conscious of this or acts unconsciously, or magically. Every act of the physician has a deep interpersonal meaning."

29. Bally, *op. cit.,* p. 485, points out that in the treatment which regards illness as only a symptom of a physical or psychic disturbance the sick person himself is not encountered.

30. Pauly-Wissova (ed.), *Real-Encyclopädie der Classischen Altertumwissenschaft* (Stuttgart, 1931) 4:1, 1081:30; O. Andersen (ed.), *Kirke-Leksikon for Norden* (Copenhagen, 1929): *"symbolon,* Lat. *Symbolum,* a sign or a mark which makes it possible to know something. The word witnesses to that ancient habit of guests (friends who enjoyed one an-

other's hospitality) to legitimate themselves by showing a piece of something. Such a mark of identification (*tessara hospitalitatis*) was passed on as a heritage from one generation to another. By putting the pieces together one was able to show the legitimacy of the person who brought the piece" (p. 444).

31. Cf. Bonhoeffer, *SC*, p. 52: Together with animals, man possesses the instincts of imitation, of submission, of sociability, and especially of hunger and of sexuality. Specifically human communion exists first of all where the conscious human spirit functions.

32. Cf. Bonhoeffer, *SC*, pp. 60 ff.: "If the communion is essentially a communion of life, the community is based on rational action. The act of will to enter the community must be directly expressed and confirmed by a contract. All that is intimately personal is here excluded. An entire spiritual isolation is characteristic of the communication of wills which function toward a goal in the system of will."

33. Cf. Bonhoeffer, *SC*, p. 61: "There is no communion without community, but above all no community without a communion of wills. This is true because community is based essentially on communion."

5. *The Therapeutic Encounter with Illness*

34. See above note 10, p. 147. The most popular term among all these, the term "psychotherapy," first came into use at the beginning of the nineteenth century. Cf. Ilza Veith, "Glimpses into the History of Psychotherapy," in Moreno (ed.), *op. cit.*, p. 1. The term "psychiatry," however, comes from long ago; Socrates already called himself *iatros tēs psychēs*, "the physician of the soul," according to Maves (ed.), *op. cit.*, p. 43.

35. Aimo T. Nikolainen, *Ihminen evankeliumin valossa* (Helsinki: WSOY, 1941), pp. 16-29, in giving an exegesis of those passages in the Sermon on the Mount where the term "soul" is used (Matt. 6:25, 27, 30), states: "Soul means life, manifestly the bodily life! The concern for soul or spirit is a concern for nourishment. Soul cannot mean 'an eternal part' of man, 'a spiritual side' in him. It means existence" (p. 23).

36. Cf. Booth, *Physician Between the Spirit and the Flesh* (manuscript), hereafter referred to as *PSF*, p. 5, "Actually everything which forms part of an organism is of significance for the character of its psychological behavior. Particularly with respect to human beings we learn more and more how their lives are influenced by such diverse factors as their inherited or acquired blood chemistry, their glands, their inherited or acquired brain physiology, their physical appearance and self-image. All this constitutes the flesh of man as he is subject to the laws of nature. Thus his behavior in health and in illness is an object of science and has become predictable with varying degrees of statistical reliability. The latter is obviously never as precise as the findings of physicists in the laboratory

because there are in man too many factors which cannot be measured. Still, the reliability is high enough to make effective methods of prophylaxis and therapy possible."

37. The expression psychological is one of the most obscure terms in modern language. In this study its content is analyzed in many connections. It is important to emphasize that we are not dealing with those therapeutic approaches in which the psychic is thought to be a special "psychological" or "spiritual" force or energy which causes illnesses or heals them. Such approaches are mentioned only when they disclose something essential about the reality of illness. Such an approach usually proclaims more the content of a special doctrine of the therapists in question than the message of disease. See, e.g., Walter Bromberg, *The Mind of Man: A History of Psychotherapy and Psychoanalysis* (New York: Harper, 1959), pp. 114-45, a presentation of mesmerism, of faith healing, of the Christian Science movement, and of occultic healing methods, etc.

38. Gerhard Kittel (ed.), *Theologisches Wörterbuch zum Neuen Testament* (Stuttgart: Kohlhammer Verlag, 1933—) III, 128 ff.: 'The characteristic trend is that in the word *therapeuō* is expressed the willingness and readiness to serve and the personal relationship of the one who serves to the other whom he serves."

6. *The Prophetic Situation in a Sick Reality*

39. An analysis of the content of Eastern Christianity, the Greek Orthodox tradition, remains outside the limited scope of this study. The influence of Eastern Christianity on the development of Western Christianity is of such a nature that just as it is impossible to understand Protestantism without its Roman Catholic background, so is it virtually impossible fully to understand the structure of Western Christianity apart from its organic correspondence to Eastern Christianity. This is evident, for example, in our studies of unity as communion. The considerations here advanced lead by their inner logic to exactly those questions which caused the division of Christianity into East and West. See the report of the conference of Greek Orthodox and Protestant theologians at the church institute in Järvenpää, Finland in May, 1958, where the concepts of catholicity and of *sobornost* were the main subjects of discussion; Aarne Siirala, "Ekumenian rintamalta" ("From the Ecumenical Front"), *Vartija*, No. 5 (1959), pp. 116 ff.

40. This forming of words occurs in a multidimensional network of life. Words grow out of events. For example, Gerhard von Rad emphasizes that the message of the Old Testament prophets has to be examined in its organic relation to the whole culture's forming of words. In a lecture at Union Theological Seminary, March 1, 1961, he pointed out the significance of the feasts, which originally followed the rhythm of nature, and

gradually became prophetic when they took on a more cultic character. Through the feasts events became integrated into history; people began to experience in them a fulfillment of a series of historical events. The feasts were a first step in a process which led toward a fuller understanding of history as a unity and as a drama. At first the different series of events were celebrated in different places. Gradually, however, this forming of words and this awareness and conceiving of events as history was experienced in common, as something which created communion. The prophets based their message of the necessity of God's new deeds upon this forming of words and upon this understanding of history. Cf. von Rad, *Genesis* (Philadelphia: Westminster, 1961), chap. 1.

41. *Gottes Gebot bei Martin Luther* (Helsinki and Stuttgart: Luther-Agricola Gesellschaft, 1956), by Aarne Siirala, examines Luther's interpretation of the state of affairs here characterized as "prophetic," as well as Luther's concept of the living word. The outline of the prophetic situation in the present study is based in part on that analysis of Luther's theology. See especially the chapter (pp. 105-36) which discusses: "God commands man to listen to His word. In obedience to the second commandment man is justified *solo verbo.*"

42. Kittel (ed.), *op. cit.,* VI, 781 ff. Cf. Joseph Sittler, "The Structure of Christian Ethics," in Harold C. Letts (ed.), *Christian Social Responsibility* (Philadelphia: Muhlenberg, 1957), I, 4, who gives a good definition of the prophet: "The figure of the prophet . . . is the unsilenceable recollection of man's structurally given existence before God."

43. When in *The Psychological Frontiers of Society* (New York: Columbia Univ., 1945) Abram Kardiner attempts to construct a theory of the forming of cultures on the basis of dynamic psychology, one of his central theses is that religious organizations, being developed and sustained by societies, codify those values which a society considers most essential for the preservation of its culture. The image of God which becomes predominant contains all the characteristics the cultural community in question would like to see in all its members. The religious institutions, which balance social and mental hygiene factors in a society, mirror the collective personality structure of the culture; they keep the members of a cultural community conscious of the total demands of their culture.

44. The British "Freudian" Edward Glover states in *Freud or Jung?* (New York: Meridian, 1960), p. 44, that the representatives of dynamic psychology have taken upon themselves a heavy responsibility. In trying to find means to regulate primitive forces without thereby impairing man's ability to adapt himself to nature and to his social environment, dynamic psychology is trying to solve the basic questions of humanity.

45. The prophetic function is always therapeutic as well. In every community the attempt is made to express through some kind of symbols,

verbal or nonverbal, what is thought to be worth teaching—what is considered healthy and genuine. The common world of symbols (e.g., flags,
public buildings, honorary titles, national festivals) can be motivated in
many different ways: religiously, scientifically, ideologically, etc. "All cultures have a therapeutic function so far as they are systems of symbolic integration—whether these systems are called religions, philosophies, ideologies, or values," according to Rieff in "A Schema of Therapeutic Types,"
a paper presented at the 1961 meeting of the American Psychological Association. Cf. the analysis of *The Republic* of Plato as a system of symbols, in Walther Riese, *The Conception of Disease: Its History, Its Versions, and Its Nature* (New York: Philosophical Library, 1953), hereafter
referred to as *CD*, pp. 4-8, 100-101.

"We learn that Asclepius revealed the art of medicine for the benefit
of people of sound constitution who normally led a happy life, but had
contracted some definite ailment. 'He would rid them of their disorders
by means of drugs or the knife and tell them to go on living as usual, so
as not to impair their usefulness as citizens' "; *The Republic*, trans.
Francis Macdonald Cornford (Oxford, 1942), p. 95.

46. Cf. Booth, *PSF*, "Religious formulations and myths are 'fantasy' only in
the sense in which the concepts of modern physics are fantasy. They are
symbolic formulations, which are necessary for the description of events
which partly transcend our four-dimensional sensual perceptions." Many
cultural critics of our time have called attention to the tendency in both
East and West to identify ourselves with the basic trends of the culture.
This means a gradual paralysis of the prophetic function of the religious
communities. The result of such an identification is some fixed form of
religion; it may then be a Greek Orthodox collectivism" or "Protestant
capitalism" or something else.

47. Cf. Paul Tillich, *The Protestant Era* (Chicago: Univ. of Chicago,
1948), hereafter referred to as *PE*, p. xxxvii, ". . . Christianity is final
only in so far as it has the power of criticising and transforming each of
its historical manifestations; and just this power is the Protestant principle." Copyright 1948 by The University of Chicago.

48. This is emphasized especially in the work of the Evangelical Academies.
Cf. Eberhard Müller (ed.), *Seelsorge in der Modernen Gesellschaft* (Hamburg: Furche Verlag, 1961); Aarne Siirala, "Wege zum Mitmenschen,"
Dokumente, Heft 3, 1957, pp. 236 ff., and "The Meaning of Illness,"
op. cit., pp. 153 ff.

49. In his description of the eschatological character of the proclamation
of the Old Testament prophets von Rad states that time is itself content;
different times have their own content. (In fact the saying "the challenge
of the time" has its roots in the Old Testament!) The prophets fought
particularly against the tendency of the people to base their lives only

on the content of time past (Isaiah 43:18 ff.). Israel's guilt roused the prophets to see that God's new deeds and times are necessary for the realization of God's election. If the events of salvation are experienced only as past history of salvation, if there is no openness to God's new deeds and times, then man has failed really to understand the purpose of God's acts of salvation in history. The content of past time is fruitful only when it is brought into fulfillment in subsequent time. (From the lecture by von Rad at Union Theological Seminary, March 1, 1961.) Cf. von Rad, *loc. cit.*,

Cf. also Rendtorff (*Evangelische Kirchenlexikon,* ed. Heinz Brunotte and Otto Weber Vol. P-Z, p. 394,) who emphasizes in his analysis of the false prophets that the texts of the Old Testament show that there are no final criteria for distinguishing between true and false prophets.

Buber, *Der Glaube der Propheten* (Zurich: Manesse Verlag, 1950), hereafter referred to as *GP,* p. 177, describes the prophetic word as a word which is powerless and weak compared to the alternatives set by men: "His prophet, this man without office, without influence, weak and shy, pronounces His word undismayed even to martyrdom, he is 'as His mouth'; whereas the mouth itself, God's mouth, is silent towards the people. God will speak to them only in the language of history, and in such a way that they will be able to explain sufficiently what happened to them by the coincidence of adverse circumstances. This God makes it burdensome for the believer and light for the unbeliever; and His revelation is nothing but a different form of hiding His face."

50. Cf. *Christ and Time,* pp. 288 ff.: "The Holy Spirit must lead to the walking in the Spirit . . . (The) working of the Holy Spirit shows itself chiefly in the 'testing' (*dokimazein*), that is in the *capacity of forming the correct Christian ethical judgment at each given moment . . .* This 'testing' is the key of all New Testament ethics. Thus Paul writes in Rom. 12:2 'Be ye transformed by the renewing of your mind, in order that you may attain the *dokimazein,* the capacity to distinguish what God's will is . . .' This 'testing' rests upon the connection of judicial thought with spontaneous inspiration. 'Quench not the spirit. Despise not prophesyings, but test all things, and hold fast that which is good' (I Thess. 5:19 ff.)." From *Christ and Time* by Oscar Cullman, trans. Floyd V. Filson. Copyright 1950, W. L. Jenkins. The Westminster Press. Used by permission.

CHAPTER 2.   THE ENCOUNTER WITH ILLNESS IN THE LIGHT
OF ITS HISTORY

1. *The Voice of Illness in the Origins of Christian Prophecy*

1. In 1956 the United States government gave a grant to the National Institute of Mental Health for research in the training of ministers so that
they would be as effective as possible in mental health work. The grant
was given to three universities (Harvard, Protestant; Loyola, Roman Catholic; Yeshiva, Jewish) which then established a special research team to
examine the problems in question. (In the last section of this book we
shall return to the Harvard report.) The director of the program at Harvard, Dr. Hans Hofmann, has edited two books which give a good description of the American discussions on these questions: *The Ministry and
Mental Health* (New York: Association, 1960) and *Religion and Mental
Health* (New York: Harper, 1961). See also Anton T. Boisen, *Exploration of the Inner World: A Study of Mental Disorder and Religious Experience* (New York: Harper, 1936) and *Out of the Depths: An Autobiographical Study of Mental Disorder and Religious Experience* (New
York: Harper, 1960); Seward Hiltner, *Religion and Health* (New York:
Macmillan, 1943); Maves (ed.), *op. cit.;* Tillich, "On Healing," *Pastoral
Psychology,* Vol. VI (1955), "Psychoanalysis, Existentialism and Theology,"
ibid., Vol. IX (1958), and *TC;* and Daniel Day Williams, *The Minister
and the Care of Souls* (New York: Harper, 1961).

2. We are limiting ourselves to an examination of the significance of the
therapeutic encounter with illness for theological studies. However the
task of Christian theology may be defined, in asking questions it cannot
avoid making decisions about the context of word forming in our time.
Cf. Tillich, *Systematic Theology, op. cit.,* I, 7, "Even kerygmatic theology
must use the conceptual tools of its period. It cannot simply repeat biblical
passages. Even when it does, it cannot escape the conceptual situation of the
biblical writers. Since the language is the basic and all-pervasive expression
of every situation, theology cannot escape the problem of the 'situation.' "

3. The biblical material concerning healing has been examined systematically, e.g., by Johannes Hempel, *Heilung als Symbol und Wirklichkeit
im biblischen Schrifttum* (Göttingen: Vandenhoeck und Ruprecht, 1958).

4. The words which mean salvation and healing are in many Western languages derived from the same root, a word which means wholeness, oneness, something which is not yet split, crooked, perverted, but is healthy,
whole. The Greek word *sōtēria* is derived from the word *saōs,* the Latin
word *salvatio* from *salvus,* and the German *Heiland* from *heil,* which
comes close to the English "healing." Cf. Tillich, "Relation of Religion
and Health: Historical Considerations and Theological Questions" ("Papers
from the University Seminar on Religion"; New York: Columbia Univ.,
1945-46), hereafter referred to as *RRH,* p. 349.

5. The concept of illness as a cosmic reality is also found in temple manuscripts which describe therapeutic methods, discovered in the ruins of the temple of Asclepius in Epidaurus. Cf. E. and L. Edelstein, *Asclepius: A Collection and Interpretation of the Testimonies* (Baltimore: Johns Hopkins, 1945). The temples provided therapy which dealt with the whole man. The therapeutic methods of the Asclepian temples included, states Masserman, diets, changing of moist and dry air, and of hot and cold air, massage, drugs, shocks, operations, group therapy based on music and drama, philosophical discussions, interpretation of dreams, and various religious rituals; Jules H. Masserman, "A Historical-Biodynamic Integration of Psychotherapy," in Moreno (ed.), *op. cit.,* III, 190 ff.

6. Tillich, *RRH,* p. 350.

7. The care of the sick among the ancient Jews obviously had no significant impact on the development of Western medicine. There were very few physicians. The central functions in taking care of the sick belonged to the priests who functioned among other things as hygiene officers of a sort. The impact of ancient Jewish culture on the care of the sick was primarily social, for illness was experienced as illness of the whole community and the attempt was made to encounter it with united efforts. Cf. Kenneth Walker, *The Story of Medicine* (London, 1959), p. 31. When the significance of the Old Testament for medicine and for the care of the sick has been analyzed, it has frequently been stated that the commandment which deals with the rhythm between work and rest and with the hallowing of the Sabbath has been the most important contribution. Cf. Peter Ritchie Calder, *Medicine and Man* (New York: New American Library, 1959), p. 58.

8. The material of the New Testament which expresses the unity of therapy and prophecy has been represented from many angles by Leslie Weatherhead, *Psychology, Religion and Healing* (New York: Abingdon-Cokesbury, 1951) and by Daniel Day Williams, *op. cit.* See also Pedro L. Entralgo, *Mind and Body* (New York: Kenedy, 1954), pp. 70 ff., who classifies the passages of the New Testament which deal with illness and healing in the following way: 1) "metaphorical" passages, where faith in Christ is described as the way from illness to health; (2) "literal" passages, which tell of the encounter of Jesus and of the apostles with various kinds of illness; and (3) "didactic" passages, where Christians are taught how to find a right relationship toward the sick and toward illness. In other respects Entralgo arranges his questions according to the classical scholastic tradition and examines the relationship between theology and medicine in the categories of the natural and supernatural.

9. The words *sōzō* and *sōtēria,* which mean "to save" and "salvation," occur in about 150 new Testament passages. More than one third of these passages deal with the healing of illnesses and with salvation from physical

death. Cf. Wheeler H. Robinson, *Redemption and Revelation* (New York: Harper, 1942), p. 232 and Daniel Day Williams, *op. cit.*, p. 15.

10. The history of therapy shows that in most cultures there have been periods when physicians and healers have been considered either gods or beings descended from gods who have a specially close relationship with the divine. In China the skills of healing have been thought to come to men through rulers of heavenly origin in previous millennia. The Japanese chronicles describe the goddess of the sun as the mother of the first healers. In India it is believed that medicinal skills stem from the Healer-Buddha. In present-day Tibet the temples of this Buddha are the only centers where medicine is taught and therapy is practiced. In Egypt Imhotep, who was worshiped as the builder of the first pyramid, was the outstanding healer for a thousand years (the second millennium before Christ). Contemporary with Imhotep there arose in Greece the divine healer Asclepius. In the histories of therapy the temples of Asclepius are mentioned as the cradle of Western therapy, the life and writings of Hippocrates, the father of medicine, being closely connected with that temple tradition. Cf. Veith, *op. cit.*, pp. 1 ff.; Moreno (ed.), *op. cit.*, I, 188 ff.; and Lauri Honko, "Varhaiskantaiset taudinselitykset ja parantamisnäytelmä" ("Primitive Interpretations of Illness and the Healing Drama"), in Jouko Hautala (ed.), *Jumin keko* (Helsinki: Suomalaisen Kirjallisuuden Seura, 1960), p. 99, who writes: "In many cultures the position of 'healer' is much more extensive than the mere task of preventing illness would seem to suppose. They have become the ones who possess the deepest wisdom and knowledge, experts in religious life, even creative poets and preservers of traditional poetry, myths, magic, etc. . . . The healer is thus a real seer and wise man." See also Uno Harva, *Suomalaisten muinaisusko* ("The Ancient Beliefs of the Finns") (Porvoo, 1948) and Martti Haavio, *Väinämöinen* (Porvoo, 1950).

2. *The Voice of Illness Is Stifled*

11. When in the following we speak of a study of history from the therapeutic viewpoint, we mean a study of the history of the care of the sick, which has developed out of the therapeutic encounter with illness. As a typical example of such a study we use the presentation of the history of medical psychology by Zilboorg and Henry, who examine mental illness and encounter with it as phenomena in which are mirrored the inner conflicts of the cultural and social life of various times: "The mentally ill reflected the cataclysmic cultural and social conflicts of the time. They were the true, although pathological, mirrors of the inner pains with which the humanity had to pay for the changes. . ." (*HMP*, p. 255).

12. See above, p. 45 f. There has also been discussion from the therapeutic viewpoint of the illnesses of the prophets. Jaspers, for example, has tried to show that some of the prophets were schizophrenic. Kütemeyer points

out in this connection that Jaspers has ignored an important viewpoint in his studies. It is true, Kütemeyer states, that the prophecies and schizophrenia are in many respects similar. Jaspers has ignored, however, the fact that schizophrenia has the character of a prophecy. Thus Jaspers makes of the prophet a mentally ill person, instead of studying the prophetic elements in that situation which often is considered only sick; Wilhelm Kütemeyer, "Einleitung," in Martti Siirala, op. cit., p. 17.

13. In an advanced seminar at Columbia University during 1945-46 which examined the relationship of religion and health, Tillich presented his opinion that the healing of mental illness is, according to the writings of the New Testament, one of the most central signs of the coming of the era of salvation: "The healing of mental illness is the most crucial proof of salvation" (RRH, p. 352). Tillich referred in this connection especially to those passages in the New Testament which tell of the casting out of demons, e.g., Matt. 12:28: "But if it is by the Spirit of God that I cast out demons, then the kingdom of God has come upon you."

14. Zilboorg and Henry, HMP, pp. 28 ff. Theological discussions which deal with the treatment of the mentally ill frequently mention Lev. 20:27 as a central biblical passage which contains a guiding principle: "Any man or woman who is a medium or a wizard must be put to death, stoned to death: their blood shall be on their own heads" (Moffatt's Translation). Cf. Zilboorg and Henry, HMP, p. 29. Zilboorg's viewpoint in examining the history of medicine is, however, so narrow that the influence of the Bible in the history of the treatment of the mentally ill receives very little attention (see, e.g., pp. 30-41). Nonetheless, his observations on the negative attitudes of the churches are valuable.

15. Zilboorg and Henry, "The Great Decline," HMP, pp. 94 ff. See also Paul Diepgen, Geschichte der Medizin (Berlin, 1914), II, 8 ff.

16. In examining the contribution of Galen to the history of medical psychology Zilboorg states: "It was a kind of summary of . . . the classical period in medicine . . . The Dark Ages in medical history began with the death of Galen in A.D. 200" (HMP, p. 90). Diepgen on the other hand states that the church contributed to the occurrence of the "great decline" in medicine and in the care of the sick (op. cit., II, 9). The earliest years of church history are usually omitted from these studies, although their influence on the later developments has been of great importance. Cf. Adolf von Harnack, Medizinisches aus der aeltesten Kirchengeschichte (Leipzig: Hinrichs, 1892).

17. There are also exceptions. Especially has the use of Old Testament material in Christianity been seen as one of the factors in creating the "dark centuries." This kind of claim, however, says more about the person who makes it than it does about the facts. Cf., e.g., J. B. Bury, A History of Freedom of Thought (New York: Holt, 1913), p. 54, ". . . how history

might have been altered . . . if the Christians had cut Jehovah out of their program."

18. Zilboorg describes the centuries from 200 to 1800 as a time when demonology ruled medical psychology (*HMP*, p. 98).

19. Zilboorg cites Origen and Cyprian as examples. According to Zilboorg, Origen's writings against Celsus pit a fanatic dogmatism against the scientific traditions of Alexandria: "The Christian Father Origen, who was not an exception in this general opposition to objective knowledge, is a case in point . . . He wrote a treatise against Celsus. He stated that 'the splendid being Raphael had special care of the sick and infirm' " (*HMP*, pp. 98 ff.). Concerning Cyprian Zilboorg states: "Religious debates and metaphysical contentions took precedence over the empirical traditions in medicine" (p. 99). It is typical of the American tradition of therapy which Zilboorg represents to see dogmatic belief and objective knowledge based on empirical facts as a crucial polarity in the history of ideas in Western culture. The Spanish student of the history of medicine, Entralgo, interprets the discussion between Origen and Celsus in quite a different way (*op. cit.*, pp. 92 ff.).

20. Among the obstacles to a therapeutic encounter with mental illness mentioned by Zilboorg are the interpretations concerning the fall into sin and the salvation from it which became dominant in Christianity. When the story of the fall into sin (Gen., chap. 3) became the basic explanation for all human distress, illness—especially mental illness—was considered as a reality to be encountered as sin. Salvation was thus considered, according to Zilboorg, in a mystical religious manner, leaving no place for a therapeutic encounter which could be empirically tested. The theological theories concerning mental illness and the mystical religious methods which became dominant in the care of mentally ill both hindered the growth of a therapeutic encounter with illness in Christianity. (*HMP*, p. 98).

21. Many of the physicians who fought for the mentally ill did it in Christ's name against the ecclesiastical and theological traditions of their times. Zilboorg finds it surprising that the shattering of ideologies which oppressed the sick was done not "by apostates and freethinkers, but by the pious and devout" (*HMP*, p. 278). One example mentioned is Agrippa, a doctor of medicine, jurisprudence, and theology, who was in opposition to the persecution of the mentally ill. He tried to show that persecution and Christianity are in irreconcilable conflict. Agrippa published a book in 1532, *De incertitudine et vanitate scientiarum et artium atque excellentia verbi dei declamatio*. Bromberg, *op. cit.*, pp. 85 ff, emphasizes the contribution of the Quakers. For example, Benjamin Rush, an American pioneer in therapeutic encounter with illness who has been called the father of American psychiatry, was a Quaker. Veith, *op. cit.*, pp. 1 ff., states that

many of those who have been advocates of human treatment of the mentally ill have derived their ideas from sources foreign to Christian faith, mentioning as examples Pinel, a Frenchman, and Chiarugi, an Italian, who drew upon the ideas of the French revolution.

22. Cf. Zilboorg and Henry, *HMP*, pp. 103 ff. The studies of Zilboorg are conditioned by the thought categories of the Enlightenment. Thus he says that the persecutions were caused by the strengthening of the mystical and dogmatic movement and by the lack of scientific spirit. Cf. Jan Ehrenwald, *From Medicine Man to Freud* (New York: Dell, 1956), p. 126: "Once the bonfires of the Inquisition were extinguished and the smoke of the burning flesh cleared from the village greens and the market places of Europe and the New World, the stage was set for the advent of a new humanistic era, followed by the technological and scientific achievements of Western culture." It is somewhat surprising that it is possible to write in such a way in the midst of the "smoke of the burning flesh" of the concentration camps of our own time.

23. Zilboorg describes the growth of the therapeutic encounter with illness as a freedom from the prison of religious and theological ideas. (*HMP*, p. 98).

24. See, e.g., Daniel Day Williams, *op.cit.*, p. 15, "The Christian faith has always recognized the obligation to 'feed the hungry and clothe the naked,' to visit the sick. . ." Olsen points to history to show that sorcery, magic, and superstition were at times the characteristics of psychotherapy; Peder Olsen, *Pastoral Care and Psychotherapy* (Minneapolis: Augsburg, 1961), p. 7.

25. For example, in his general summary of the history of pastoral care, McNeill does not examine the history of the treatment of the mentally ill. The hostile attitude toward the mentally ill and direct persecution of them which has occurred during church history in many forms is not studied as a phenomenon which belongs to church history. In describing medieval hospitals supported by churches, McNeill states that the sick were treated with care and commitment; only the mentally ill were the exception: "But this is less true of the treatment of the mental cases, where the presupposition of diabolical possession was an obstacle; "A Religious Healing of Soul and Body," in Maves (ed.), *op. cit.*, p. 53. This is almost all he says about the role of the churches in persecutions either here or in his *History of the Cure of Souls* (New York: Harper, 1951). There is often an inconsistency at this point in the studies of church history, for the material is chosen arbitrarily. If, for example, the growth of hospitals during the Middle Ages is considered to be caused by the churches because it happened within the framework of organized churches, it would be consistent to examine the Inquisition and the persecution of witches in the same light.

26. The voices raised from the point of view of therapy against the perversion of prophecy have often been silenced in the common history of therapy and prophecy. The writings of Johannes Weyer, who has been called the father of modern psychiatry, are a case in point. As a physician his conclusion was that the witches were mentally ill. In his book *De praestigiis daemonum* (1536), Weyer claimed that persecutors should be punished instead of poor sick people. Weyer was also opposed to the treatment of the mentally ill as criminals. When Zilboorg describes the lifework of Weyer he says that Weyer was aware that the task of psychiatry was to protect the sick person from oppression based on political prejudices, theological traditions, or formal interpretation of the law. Weyer stated accordingly that the physician who defends the sick has to be prepared to meet resistance especially from theologians and from lawyers. Weyer wrote that he knew the theologians would say that his writings went beyond the limits of his vocation when he based his conclusions on biblical passages. He replied: "My only answer will be that I shall say nothing else but that St. Luke the Evangelist was a physician in Antioch . . ." (Zilboorg and Henry, *HMP*, p. 233).

27. *Ibid.*, p. 141.

28. Medical studies in mental illness were then especially directed to an examination of the influence of the phenomena of nature on mental illnesses: "The medical man . . . turned to the universe he could at least see with his own eyes, to the sun, the moon, the stars . . . this was an expression of an intuitive need to correlate the problems of human illness with the system of nature" (Zilboorg and Henry, *HMP*, p. 136).

29. *Malleus Maleficarum* was first published around 1490. During the following centuries there were about twenty reprints of it. For centuries it was the normative book for dealing with witchcraft in the Roman Catholic church. Cf. Montague Summers (ed.), *Malleus Maleficarum* (Suffolk, 1928), Foreword; Zilboorg and Henry, *HMP*, pp. 150 ff.; Ehrenwald, *op. cit.*, pp. 114 ff.; and Charles Williams, *Witchcraft* (New York: Meridian, 1960), pp. 123 ff.

30. The members of the theological faculty at the University of Cologne confirmed the treatise with their signatures. Sprenger and Kramer also received the official confirmation of the emperor for their action (Zilboorg and Henry, *HMP*, pp. 150 ff.).

31. Ehrenwald, *op. cit.*, p. 141, states that *Malleus Maleficarum* contains much material of value from the viewpoint of psychoanalysis: it is aware of the relationship between sexual instincts and mental illness, it emphasizes the significance of unconscious life, and it describes women who try to deprive men of their masculinity as the prototypes of witches.

32. There are three main sections in *Malleus Maleficarum*. The first deals with three elements which are considered to belong necessarily to witch-

craft: the devil, the witch, and the providence of God; Summers (ed.), *op. cit.*, p. 1. The second main section is devoted to the study of the substance of witchcraft. The question of how the forces of witchcraft operate and how one can undo the influence of witches is examined (p. 89). The third section tells how witches and all heretics should be treated both in secular and ecclesiastical courts, (p. 194). The writers begin their book by answering the question whether the belief in the existence of witches is essential to the Catholic faith and whether one who claims the opposite can be considered a heretic, (p. 1). The writers answer their own question in the affirmative and state their reasons for their stand by referring both to divine and to human law, (p. 3). Using many biblical quotations they try to show that the divine law commands not only to avoid witches but also to kill them, (p. 3). The writers conclude that faith demands that everybody who errs strongly in the interpretation of the Bible has to be considered a heretic, and therefore everybody who denies the existence of witchcraft, which is an essential assertion of the faith of the Holy Roman Church, is a heretic, (p. 4). Cf. the presentation by Summers of the origins of *Malleus Maleficarum* (pp. xx ff.).

33. Charles Williams, *op. cit.*, p. 124. In the Foreword of the English translation of *Malleus Maleficarum*, the translator, Summers, characterizes the strivings of the witches by saying that they tried to abolish the authority of rulers and kings, private property, marriage, and religion. If one does not take into account that the Inquisition had to fight such enemies, Summers says, it might be difficult to understand fully the methods of the Inquisition, which were "a little drastic." Summers seems to consider the theological motivations of the Inquisition convincing: "There can be no doubt that had this most excellent tribunal continued to enjoy its full prerogative and the full exercise of its salutary powers, the world at large would be in a far happier and far more orderly position today" (*op. cit.*, p. xviii).

34. *Ibid.*, pp. 85 ff. Cf. Ehrenwald, *op. cit.*, pp. 116-18, who gives to the section where the material of *Malleus Maleficarum* is presented the rubric: "The Bonfires of the Inquisition against Mental Disease."

35. Summers, *op. cit.*, pp. 194 ff. Cf. Ehrenwald, *op. cit.*, pp. 139-41. Zilboorg and Henry, *HMP*, p. 259, mention as one example an event from Germany in the year 1636. Somebody imagined that he was God the Father; his tongue was cut out, his head was severed from his body, and finally he was burned at the stake.

36. *Ibid.*, pp. 152 ff., 314. Ehrenwald, *op. cit.*, pp. 123 ff., who states in his comments on the text of *Malleus Maleficarum* that the texts contain many descriptions of the mental illnesses of that time, filled with fine nuances. The diagnostic observations of Sprenger and Kramer are often to the point. Their basic error lay, according to Ehrenwald, in the treatment

they recommended, whereby they fought superstition with the forces of superstition. The persecutions of witches were symptoms of the same collective disease, mass hysteria, which was expressed in the phenomenon called witchcraft. The persecutors projected their own sadistic instincts on the witches and made them a minority group which the majority needed as its scapegoat (p. 141).

37. Cf. Zilboorg, *The Medical Man and the Witch during the Renaissance* (Baltimore: John Hopkins, 1935) and Veith, *op. cit.*

38. Bromberg, *op. cit.,* pp. 38 ff., emphasizes the significance of the monasteries in the history of psychotherapy: "The monastic tradition of treatment through loving care and gentleness was particularly applicable to mental cases" (p. 39). See also Wright, "Medieval Attitudes toward Mental Illness," *Bull. Hist. Med.,* VII (1939), 352.

39. A careful picture of the attempts of early Christianity to meet mental illness in the name of humanity is given in the collected works published by Caelius Aurelianus in the fifth century. His work has been published in English as, *On Acute Diseases and on Chronic Diseases* (Chicago, 1950).

40. Zilboorg, e.g., has nothing to tell about the relationship of the Reformation to demonology except a short notice of a letter from Melanchthon to Calvin which congratulates Calvin for executing a sentence to burn someone at the stake. Without giving any proof, Zilboorg states that Calvin and Luther followed the traditions of *Malleus Maleficarum* (*HMP*, pp. 166, 174).

41. The inner struggle of Luther has been presented from this point of view in a careful way by Erik H. Erikson, *Young Man Luther*: *A Study in Psychoanalysis and History* (New York: Norton, 1958).

42. Zilboorg does not pay any attention to the Reformers' fight against the "angels of darkness." He mentions in this respect only Johann Weyer, called the founder of modern psychiatry, who stated sarcastically in his book *Pseudomonarchia Daemonum* (1583) that he had found in the material he had studied seventy-two Princes of Darkness and more than seven million smaller devils (*HMP*, p. 163). When history is described from such a point of view, it is not surprising that the history of the Protestant Inner Mission, for example, is left outside the study, although it has had a great influence on the history of the encounter with illness in general and with mental illness in particular. Cf. McNeill, *A History of the Cure of Souls, op. cit.* The history of therapy written by Bromberg is also a telling example of this kind of "dogmatic" examination of history. Bromberg's view, which strongly colors his interpretation of history, is "psychological" in the sense that he understands the psyche as a special force. He interprets faith as a psychic force which has to be taken into account alongside other factors which have influence upon illness and health. When Bromberg characterizes the contribution of Christianity to the history of therapy he

calls it "faith-healing": "The modification of faith-healing stimulated by the spread of Christianity in the Western world consisted in a refinement of the vehicle of faith. Jesus taught that faith alone was enough . . . healing by direct faith was an even further simplification of psychotherapy beyond the various symbolic vehicles of healing" (*op. cit.,* p. 22). When Bromberg later speaks of the return of faith-healing (pp. 114-15), he combines in one chapter Mesmerism (animal magnetism), Latter-Day Faith-Healers, the Christian Science movement, miracle healers, the care of souls, and pastoral psychology.

43. McNeill does not examine as a part of church history the persecution of the mentally ill which took place within Christianity. He states rather that the inhuman trends in hospitals for the mentally ill resulted from the estrangement of those institutions from Christianity: "The secularization of institutions for the insane apparently drove out of them most elements of compassion and humanism"; "A Religious Healing of Soul and Body," in Maves (ed.), *op. cit.,* p. 59.

3. *The Voice of Illness Is Ignored*

44. Zilboorg and Henry, *HMP,* p. 41, characterizes this world-image as that of theurgic mysticism, stating: "The medical man had to wait many centuries, almost until our own day, before he was able to approach the human mind with any degree of certainty that neither the philosopher nor the theologian would look upon him as an intruder into a field he should not aspire to plow. . ." According to Zilboorg the two things which have stifled the therapeutic encounter are the religiosity of theurgic mysticism and abstract philosophy.

45. Entralgo, *op. cit.,* pp. 21 ff.

46. *Ibid.,* p. 27, analyzes the expression *shertu* which was used in the Assyro-Babylonian world for sin, moral impurity, the wrath of gods, punishment, and illness, and states that illness was primarily *shertu,* a moral impurity which hindered the sick from participating in religious rituals. The sick were those persons who had caused their own excommunication. Physical symptoms such as fever, wounds, or paralysis, were considered as expressions of the moral impurity which was behind all the symptoms.

47. Cf. *ibid.,* pp. 27 ff.; in describing the Assyro-Babylonian treatment of the sick, Entralgo compares it to confession. Cf. Honko, *"Varhaiskantaiset taudinselitykset ja parantamisnäytelmä,"* op. cit., p. 63: "If in some community it is believed *a priori* that illnesses are caused by value-transgression, one can say that the predominant explanation for sickness by that community is tabu-transgression. The scheme of the healing drama is then the following: first there is a hearing, which is led by the healer and in which the patient and the audience participate with their own. . . . There

the possible value transgressions, of which the patient is guilty, are examined, and it is of greatest importance that the patient openly confesses his deeds. After a thorough hearing and confession the healing of illness is to be expected. The obedience of the patient can be further emphasized by some rituals of reconciliation and purification . . . In the high cultures of the countries of the Twin Rivers this explanation for illness was central."

48. Entralgo, *op. cit.*, p. 31, refers to the concept of illness in Homer and mentions among other things the passage in the Odyssey (Book XVII, pp. 382-85), where the prophet and the healer (*ieter kakon*) are mentioned among those who possess (*demiergoi*) the common and public power to resist evil.

49. Entralgo, *op. cit.*, pp. 21-39, points out that the rites arranged in connection with the therapeutic encounter with an illness were also directed against future illnesses. These preventative rites were especially important because it was thought that man could become a prisoner of sin and illness unwittingly and unwillingly. In the rites the attempt was obviously made to influence the unconscious so that illness could be avoided. The priests and other healers were responsible for confronting the "enemy" illness strategically in a wise and proper manner. They also had to try to command the whole community in a fight against the corruptive forces in such a way that the enemy would be met on all sectors of the front. Such preventative and healing rites meant a gathering and centralization of all the forces which could resist the powers of evil behind an illness.

50. Zilboorg and Henry, *HMP*, pp. 40 ff., mention Alcmaeon, the contemporary of Pythagoras, as the first representative of empirically based physiological psychology. Entralgo, *op. cit.*, pp. 40 ff., emphasizes the significance of Homer and of pre-Socratic philosophy in the development of Greek medicine, and calls the theory of Alcmaeon the cornerstone of Western naturalistic pathology. In Alcmaeon's theory health is described as an equilibrium of the elements (moist-dry, cold-hot, bitter-sweet, etc.) of nature (*physis*), and illness (*nosos*) as a disturbance of the equilibrium in such a way that one element has become dominant (*monarkhia*).

51. Riese, *CD*, p. 5, describes Plato's concept of illness in the following way: "Disease is defined as the result of the unnatural excess of the four constituents of our body, earth, fire, water and air, or the change of any of them from its own natural place into another . . ."

52. Entralgo, *op. cit.*, pp. 43-44, points out that the physicians of the fifth century from Alcmaeon to Hippocrates sought the immediate causes of illness in the nature (*physis*) of the sick. More remote causes of illness were to be found in the changes of the relationship between the individual and universal nature. The treatment was concentrated on a regulating (*diaita*) of the individual nature of the patient so that he would regain the physical harmony he had lost.

53. The lifework and the writings of Galen in the second century were the decisive factors in the development which led to the predominance of the Hippocratic tradition in the Western world (*ibid.*, pp. 63 ff. and Zilboorg and Henry, *HMP*, pp. 92 ff.).

54. Riese, *CD*, p. 2: "The Stoic's attitude towards pain and disease springs from his primary concern to preserve the tranquility of mind, and to eliminate disturbing factors. These do not enter his view of life. . . To the Stoic life appears complete when deprived of pain and suffering, but not when containing them. That pain and disease may assume stimulating functions and open new roads, endowing the disturbed individual with unforeseen, though potentially pre-existing gifts and abilities, is a view or an experience foreign to the Stoic doctrine."

55. Abraham Kaplan, "Freud and Modern Philosophy," in Benjamin Nelson (ed.), *Freud and the Twentieth Century* (London: Allen and Unwin, 1958), p. 209, states that philosophers in their criticism of Freud often have referred to the view of the "two truths": "What the medievals distinguished as the domains of philosophy and theology, and the moderns as the realms of reason and faith, is formulated today in the dualism of 'referential' and 'emotive' meaning. Knowledge is in these terms narrowly conceived as 'referential' only and the content of art, religion and morality excluded from the province of epistemology as non-cognitive."

56. For many centuries physicians often had theological training. The theory of two parallel truths became incarnate in their persons. This theory gave a rationale for action in which the therapeutic and prophetic functions were related in an nonorganic way. Zilboorg and Henry, *HMP*, pp. 126-27, state that these "clerical physicians" in no way dealt with problems connected with the encounter with mental illness or illness in general as psychological reality. Medicine and theology existed in the same person without being related.

57. The seventeenth century is described as such a time. Literature appeared against the persecution of witches; e.g., Reginald Scot, *The Discovery of Witchcraft: Providing, that the Compacts of Witches with Devils and all Infernal Spirits or Familiars are but Erroneus Novelties and Imaginary Conceptions* (1655). The provision in French law concerning the capital punishment of witches was rescinded. Empirical research became more common in the encounter with illness. But little attention was paid to the mentally ill. There were plenty of mentally ill, states Zilboorg, in towns and villages; they wandered in the streets and on the highways; they were in prisons and cellars. They amused the people or they horrified them. The physicians could not avoid seeing them, Zilboorg continues, but it seems, nevertheless, that medicine deliberately turned away from mental illness (*HMP*, pp. 254-72).

58. The influence of the forces of witchcraft upon mental illness was discussed until the nineteenth century (Veith, *op. cit.*, pp. 1 ff).

59. Zilboorg and Henry, *HMP*, p. 250, describes the influence of Descartes in furthering the development in this direction.

60. *Ibid.*, pp. 459-60.

61. Tillich, "The Meaning of Health," *op. cit.*, characterizes this kind of encounter with illness in the following way: "Under the predominance of the physical dimension, health is the well-functioning of all the particular parts of man. Disease is the non-functioning of these parts because of incidents, infections or imbalances. Healing then is the removal of the diseased parts or their mechanical replacement: surgery. The prevalence of surgery since the Renaissance is based on an image of man (classically formulated by Descartes) which views him as a well-functioning body-machine..."

62. Zilboorg and Henry, *HMP*, p. 312, describe this by speaking of a tendency on the part of the lay and medical world to consider themselves as separate from and superior to the mentally sick, "superior by virtue of this assumed, unproven, but generally accepted state of being normal... The world considers them (the insane) stepchildren of life... Perhaps this psychological factor has survived in the human community as an atavistic but potent inheritance from those remote days when primitive peoples summarily killed the sick and the aged merely because they had become burdens to a community... It is impossible otherwise to explain the really striking fact that until the very end of the eighteenth century there were no real hospitals for the mentally sick."

63. *Ibid.*, p. 467, states that the predominance of the mechanistic view in the encounter with illness was the result, among other things, of those idealistic movements in which all things "psychological" were considered to belong to the world of "the immortal soul." This kind of thinking motivated those studies which were not based on the laws of the "supernatural" reality to examine human behavior mechanistically.

64. The theological way of asking questions is especially apparent in the writings of the psychiatrists in Central Europe at the beginning of the nineteenth century. See: Heinroth, *Lehrbuch der Störungen des Seelenlebens* (Leipzig, 1818); Groos, *Entwurf einer philosophischen Grundlage für die Lehre von den Geisteskrankheiten* (Heidelberg, 1828); and Feuchtersleben, *Lehrbuch der ärztlichen Seelenkunde* I-III (Wien, 1845). Feuchtersleben presents ideas which are of great importance from the theological point of view. He describes physical man as a "spiritualized" body and psychic man as an "incarnated" spirit. Man is a unity, an undivided one. Mental illness is psychic in that it expresses itself through the bodily senses, because the body is an "incarnation" of the soul. Cf. Zilboorg and Henry, *HMP*, p. 477.

65. Booth, "Conditions of Medical Responsibility," *op. cit.*, p. 249. Reinhold Niebuhr, "Human Creativity and Self-concern in Freud's Thought," in Nelson (ed.), *op. cit.*, says of Freud that although he represented in his thinking the traditions of the Enlightenment, in many respects he broke with its optimism. Freud's realistic view of man, Niebuhr continues, shattered that mind-body dualism which had been prevalent in Western thought from Plato and Aristotle until Spinoza and Descartes: "This dualism was informed by the assumption that the mind, if powerful enough or educated sufficiently, would be in control of all of its impulses and it would guide the self to the more inclusive rational ends which constituted the uniquely human aspect of man's life, as distinguished from the animals, who lived merely in the dimension of nature" (p. 256). This same optimism was characteristic of the French Enlightenment, although the concept of human nature rather than the concept of the human mind was in the center. Human nature, the natural survival impulse, is uncorrupted. Its perversions grow when it becomes frustrated by bad social and political institutions. The task of reason was to lead man back to nature. Cf. Riese, *CD*, pp. 11 ff., who describes Rousseau's concept of illness as the extreme opposite of the Hippocratic concept.

66. The thinking of Descartes is one example of the way philosophical struggle with this dichotomy is intertwined with the tradition of Christian prophecy. In descriptions of the history of medicine Descartes is frequently mentioned as a representative of a purely philosophical view which leads to the separation of soul and body and to a mechanistic understanding of man.

In his philosophy Descartes advocates a dichotomy between soul and body, between the spiritual and material. At the same time, however, he emphasizes their unity in immediate everyday experience. The phenomena of the world of the soul cannot be scientifically derived from phenomena in the bodily existence or vice versa, but the experience of everyday life shows that there is an organic unity between them. This unity has to be experienced in order to be understood. The understanding of the unity between soul and body belongs to the level of "existential" (a post-Descartes term) and not to the level of "scientific" knowledge. Reason can understand the laws of the psychic life and explain the laws of bodily functions, but it can only partly anticipate the connections between them. One can comprehend these connections only through sensory perception. Descartes differentiates three levels on which insights of reality can be formed: (1) metaphysics, the object of which is also the soul; (2) mathematics and physics, the object of which is matter; and (3) everyday life (that encounter with life which happens outside philosophy and science), the object of which is the unity between soul and body. The human mind is not able to grasp fully the correspondence and unity of soul and body, which must be learned by experience. As a philosopher, Descartes thus dis-

misses the discussions of the unity of soul and body. As a Roman Catholic
Christian and as a man of everyday life, however, Descartes discusses it
prolifically. For example, in his studies of the Eucharist Descartes defends
the doctrine of transubstantiation and supports his view with the statement
that the soul makes the body a whole. First the soul makes a body out of
matter. In the human body there is a continuous change by which all
parts are repeatedly replaced by new ones; it remains the "same" body only
because the soul is constant. Hence the soul of Christ can make of a piece
of bread one part of his body. C. A. van Peursen, *Leib—Seele—Geist*:
Einführung in eine phänomenologische Anthropologie (Gütersloh:
Gütersloher Verlagshaus, 1959), pp. 23-29.

However, the viewpoint of Descartes may be evaluated, it is obvious
that this system of thought cannot be properly understood if no attention
is paid to the way Descartes himself located it in the totality of human
existence.

4. *The Voice of Illness Breaks Through*

67. Cf. Erich Fromm, *Escape from Freedom* (New York: Rhinehart,
1941).

68. Cf. George C. Anderson, *Man's Right to Be Human*: *To Have Emotions Without Fear* (New York: Morrow, 1959).

69. Cf. Zilboorg and Henry, *HMP*, pp. 52 ff.

70. *Ibid.*, p. 164, points out that the word anthropology was used for the
first time by Magnus Hundt in his work concerning the structure of the
nature of man, published in 1501.

71. Zilboorg, "The Changing Concept of Man in Present-Day Psychiatry,"
in Nelson (ed.), *op. cit.,* pp. 33 ff.; Bromberg, *op. cit.,* pp. 70 ff.

72. In the year 1590 Goeckel's *Psychologia-hoc est de hominis perfectione*
was published and four years later Cassman's *Psychologia anthropologica*
appeared. They led to a psychological examination of questions of education
and adaptation to society; Zilboorg and Henry, *HMP*, p. 178.

The so-called scientific psychology, measuring mental life with methods
developed by natural sciences, is thought to have begun shortly after the
break-through of the therapeutic encounter with illness. Gustaf Fechner,
who is called the founder of scientific psychology and who published his
theses on the measuring of mental life in the year 1860, has had an important influence upon the early history of psychoanalysis; Calvin S. Hall, *A
Primer of Freudian Psychology* (New York: World, 1954), p. 11.

73. Zilboorg and Henry, *HMP*, pp. 180 ff.

74. Vives, for example, attempted to show in his book *De concordia at et
discordia in humano genere* (1529), what an important role the psychological understanding of human behavior plays in the solving of international conflicts; Zilboorg and Henry, *HMP*, p. 189.

75. Paracelsus, who wrote a significant treatise concerning the character of mental illness (1526) and refuted demonological interpretations, emphasized strongly that the divine influence becomes realized through men: "When He (the Lord) performs a miracle, He performs it humanly and through mankind; if He effects wonderful cures, He does that through men, and therefore through the physician" (*Paramirum*, I, 21); Zilboorg and Henry, *HMP*, p. 196.

76. Lessa remarks that deification of the human characteristically appears during difficult crises: William A. Lessa and Evon Z. Vogt (eds.), *Reader in Comparative Religion: An Anthropological Approach* (Evanston, Ill.: Row, Peterson, 1958), p. 314, ". . . the insecurities of Renaissance individualism were commonly alleviated by body divination. . ."

77. When the Renaissance is described in this way no attention is paid to the fact that the view of man as a microcosm which restores reality does not overcome the dichotomy in interpreting reality. The problems are only removed to the world of microcosm. The form of the questions and the medieval categories of thought (supernatural-natural, soul-body, faith-reason) remained basically intact during the Renaissance; they were only moved from cosmic dimensions to the framework of the microcosm. Gradually there developed discussion concerning the role played by the mind and the body, which were then considered separately from the soul as objects of scientific study. Salvation and healing, which had lost their cosmic dimensions, were again considered as belonging to different spheres of reality. According to Tillich, *RRH*, p. 354, "Both of them lose their cosmic character, salvation becomes concerned with the individual soul, healing with the individual body."

78. Kardiner, "Freud: The Man I Knew," in Nelson (ed.), *op. cit.*, p. 55, says that the breakthrough of the psychoanalytic movement is closely connected with the rise of liberalism. Liberalism made it possible to have a neurosis without being excommunicated from the community: "It was liberalism which gave suffering a voice and neurosis an opportunity for expression."

79. It has been said that the cornerstone of the therapeutic encounter with illness is the confession of the unrestricted value of every human being. Cf. Valer Barbu, "Psychoanalysis and Philosophy," *American Journal of Psychoanalysis*, V, No. 1 (1945), 60. Charles R. Stinette, *Faith, Freedom and Selfhood* (Greenwich, Conn.: Seabury, 1959), pp. 23 ff., emphasizes that according to therapy, freedom can be experienced only in communion with fellow beings.

80. A consequence of the release of the mentally ill from chains was the dramatic liberalization of the possibilities which had been imprisoned. The French physician Pinel, who at the very end of the eighteenth century was one of the first who dared to perform such experiments in his hospital,

described the release in the following way: "People awaited impatiently the result of the experiment. One of the patients who was led outdoors, and saw the sun exclaimed, 'Oh, how beautiful.' He was an English officer who had been incarcerated for a period of forty years; . . . after two years of remaining calm, following the liberation from his chains, the officer was allowed to leave the hospital" (Zilboorg and Henry, *HMP*, p. 323).

81. The first institutions which can be called mental hospitals came into being just before the beginning of the eighteenth century. *Ibid.*, p. 327, reads, "One may say without risk of exaggeration that it is the organization of proper mental hospitals which made the 'moral treatment,' that is to say, psychotherapy, possible."

82. *Ibid.*, p. 371.

83. At the international meeting of psychiatrists in Moscow in 1897, Krafft-Ebing spoke of "our neurotic time" and coined the expression "civilization and syphilization." Zilboorg, *ibid.*, p. 462, writes referring to these expressions "These remarks were clear indications that even the traditional . . . medical psychologists already felt that a relationship between mental disease and cultural functioning exists . . . and that the whole community life is interrelated with psychopathology."

84. Zilboorg describes the attempts of Moebius (1853-1907, contemporary with Krafft-Ebing) to show the significance of research in mental illness for various cultural fields: "The remark sounded like an intuitive premonition that . . . mental disease might prove not a pernicious deathblow and might even become the source of the very creative powers of cultural life." Concerning the representatives of the German romantic movement, Zilboorg, *ibid.*, p. 465, states that these began to examine mental illness as a phenomenon in which is hidden the key for understanding of real health.

85. *Ibid.*, p. 488; Bromberg, *op. cit.*, pp. 254 ff.

86. Bromberg, *op. cit.*, pp. 200 ff.

87. *Ibid.*, p. 216; Rollo May, Ernest Angel, and Henri Ellenberger (eds.), *Existence: A New Dimension in Psychiatry and Psychology* (New York: Basic, 1958); and Rudolf Allers, *Existentialism and Psychiatry* (Springfield, Ill.: Thomas, 1960).

88. Glover, *op. cit.*, pp. 21 ff.

89. Booth, *RFP*, pp. 51 ff. and "Conditions of Medical Responsibility," *op. cit.*

90. Cf. Erwin H. Ackerknecht, "Problems of Primitive Medicine," in Lessa and Vogt (eds.), *op. cit.*, pp. 343 ff.

CHAPTER 3. THE THERAPEUTIC ENCOUNTER WITH ILLNESS

1. *Listening to the Voice of Illness*

1. In the following, an attempt is made to give a typological sketch of the therapeutic encounter with illness. Freud has been chosen to represent therapy because he is, from the point of view of our theme, of special interest in the history of therapy. Furthermore, the impact of Freud on present discussions concerning the meaning of illness is obviously deeper and more extensive than that of other persons who have established schools of thought in this field. See Nelson (ed.), *op. cit.*, and Zilboorg and Henry, *HMP*, pp. 485 ff.

2. Cf. Tillich, "The Transition from Essence to Existence and the Symbol of 'the Fall'," *Systematic Theology, op. cit.*, II, 29 ff. Tillich adds: "Freud has shown that libidinous elements are present in the highest spiritual experiences and activities of man, and, in doing so, he has rediscovered insights which can be found in the monastic traditions . . . in early and medieval Christianity. . . It is the never satisfied libido in man, whether repressed or unrestrained, which produces in him the desire to get rid of himself as man. In these observations concerning man's 'discontent' with his creativity, Freud looks deeper into the human predicament than many of his followers and critics. Up to this point, a theological interpreter of man's estrangement is well advised to follow Freud's analyses" (pp. 53-54).

3. In Freud's lifetime important developments took place in the natural sciences. These developments had a deep impact on Freud's concepts. When Freud was three years old Darwin's great work was published. In the following year Fechner laid the foundation for a modern psychology based on the methods of the natural sciences. Also, von Helmholtz, who formulated the theory of the preservation of energy in physics, had an important influence upon Freud. Freud studied at the University of Vienna under one of the most prominent physiologists of the last century, Ernst Bruecke, who taught that the living organism is a dynamic system to which the laws of chemistry and physics can be applied. See Hall, *op. cit.*, pp. 11-13. Reinhold Niebuhr, *op. cit.*, p. 257, states of Freud that he was more naturalistic than the physiocrats. Freud, however, saw nature as more complicated than they did.

4. Zilboorg and Henry, *HMP*, p. 459, ". . . for each period of history the question of mental disease has been settled in a manner corresponding to the spirit of the age."

5. *Ibid.*, p. 463, points out how mental illness has become, through a therapeutic encounter with it, a source of creative powers and of cultural growth; also, "Mental disease became the source of a new knowledge about man" (p. 490).

6. *Ibid.*, p. 486. Charcot had had success in France in using hypnosis in the cure of hysteria; see Hall, *op. cit.*, p. 14. Concerning Zilboorg's opinion of the "revolutionary" character of Freud's lifework, as was said earlier many of the writings in the history of therapy have been one-sided. Cf. Riese, *CD*, p. 86: "The greatest step ever made in the history of medical thought was made at the very moment when the physician or his fore-runner turned to the sick person himself as to the source of therapeutical endeavor. This step was made by the Greeks."

7. Sigmund Freud, *A General Introduction to Psychoanalysis* (New York: Permabooks, 1958), hereafter referred to as *GIP*, Freud emphasized also that psychoanalysis was born when the encounters with illness had come to a dead end: "Psychoanalysis was born of medical necessity. It originated in the need of helping the victims of nervous disease to whom rest, hydrop-athy or electrical treatment could bring no relief"; "A Preface" (1917), in Nelson (ed.), *op. cit.*, p. 41. "Psychoanalysis is a medical treatment for those suffering from nervous disorders" (*GIP*, p. 19).

2. *Man Is Encountered in Illness*

8. Cf. Reinhold Niebuhr, *op. cit.*, p. 255, who advances the opinion that only an analysis of the theories of Freud is relevant for theology. He ad-mits the impact of Freud in improving the skill in healing, but does not analyze Freud's concepts from that point of view. Here we discuss Freud's theories of culture and religion only insofar as they throw light on the structure of his therapeutic encounter with illness. Dealing with Freud's theories would require that we adopt a viewpoint for which the history of ideas would determine the way to ask questions. In this respect the symposium edited by Nelson on Freud's impact upon the culture of our century, is important.

9. Jerome S. Bruner, "Freud and the Image of Man," in Nelson (ed.), *op. cit.*, p. 277, writes: "In the psychotherapy of a confused schizophrenic, as well as in the psychotherapy of a child, one has to begin by assuming a role, by representing some figure who has a central importance in the life of the sick person, in order to release the tensions in the life of the sick person in a meaningful way." Cf. Gaetano Benedetti, "Psychotherapie eines Schizophrenen," *Psyche*, IX (1955), 29-30.

10. Sigmund Freud and Joseph Breuer, *Studies in Hysteria* (Boston: Beacon, 1937), pp. 96 ff.

11. *Ibid.*, p. 103.

12. *Ibid.*, p. 106. It must be emphasized that the ministry of psychody-namics began with a psychological interpretation of a physical symptom. See Booth, *RFP*, p. 51. Cf. Benedetti, "Die Welt des Schizophrenen und deren psychotherapeutische Zugänglichkeit," *Schweiz. Med. Wochen-*

schrift, LXXXIV (1954), 1029, who emphasizes that the therapist must listen to the voice of illness, that hidden in the illness itself is the cry for healing, and adds on p. 28 of the work cited in note 9 above, "Where in this particular case is the psychotherapeutic task? It is necessary above all to realize that homosexuality here means a desperate need for communication in relationship to the father. These attempts at communication are able to use only a bodily, in a terrible way, a bodily language, because there are no other adequate possibilities of expression."

13. Freud and Breuer, *op. cit.,* p. 111.

14. Cf. Freud, *Civilization and Its Discontents* (New York: Cape & Smith, 1930), p. 24, where he states that when we love we are most defenseless toward suffering.

15. Freud and Breuer, *op. cit.,* pp. 113-14.

3. *Illness Is Encountered in Man*

16. Freud, *Origin of Psychoanalysis* (New York: Basic, 1954). See also Ehrenwald, *op. cit.,* p. 133. The letter in question, dated January, 1897, was written to Wilhelm Fliess, a close friend of Freud's.

17. Freud and Breuer, *op. cit.,* p. 114.

18. Freud, *Beyond the Pleasure Principle* (New York: Liveright, 1922, and Bantam, 1959), hereafter referred to as *BPP,* p. 92. Quoted by permission of LIVERIGHT, Publishers, N. Y.

19. Munroe, *op. cit.,* pp. 305-17.

20. *Ibid.,* p. 306. Freud gave detailed instructions warning the therapist not to be in personal contact with the patient outside ordinary therapy. The therapist has to try to avoid responding in any way to the personal fears and aspirations of the patient. The importance of the therapist's own analysis lies partly in its developing his ability to be cautious about such reactions.

21. "The expectations which are conditioned by the structure and laws of the life-image of the patient have to be denied (*versagen*) and one should not react to them according to the aspirations of the patient, if one tries to free the patient from the prison of his life-image . . . The instruction concerning *Versagung,* concerning extreme privation, could be formulated as follows: the analyst should never ignore the fact that the patient's right to live is absolute and is his original right. In this one has to be radically sincere with oneself, because everybody is inclined to put oneself in relationship to others as a life-giver. That quality in the patient which considers life to be possible only when certain requirements are fulfilled is a temptation to the analyst . . . If the analyst tries in one way or another to give the patient opportunities of living off the analyst himself, this hinders the recovery of the patient . . . *Versagung* is a sincere answer to the

question of how one can give most to the other"; Arvola, "What is psychoanalytic therapy?" (Paper given in the seminar of Therapeia-Foundation in the spring of 1960).

22. In biological research increasing attention has been paid to the correlation between the life style of various species and the development of the various parts of the brain. The structure of the human brain shows that man is in a more differentiated and more multidimensional relationship with the various elements of nature than any other animal. See Rothschild, *Das Zentralnervensystem als Symbol des Erlebens* (Basel and New York: S. Karger, 1958); cf. Booth, *PSF*.

23. In his "Problems of Authority for Individual Christians: Its Use and Abuse," *Journal of Pastoral Care*, IX (1952), 212 ff., as in his *PSF*, Booth criticizes Fromm's conception of "human nature." Cf. Fromm, *Man for Himself* (New York: Rinehart, 1947), pp. 76 ff.

4. *Illness and the Word*

24. Freud, *GIP*, p. 25.

25. *Ibid.*, p. 26.

26. *Ibid.*, pp. 21-22, states that there is no more to psychoanalytic treatment than an exchange of words between the patient and the therapist. For the most part, the patient speaks and the therapist listens. Through words, Freud continues, one can give the other the greatest happiness or lead him to utter despair.

27. Bromberg, *op. cit.*, pp. 200 ff.

28. Boss, "Daseinsanalytische Bemerkungen zu Freuds Vorstellung des Unbewussten," *op. cit.*, pp. 130 ff.

29. Hobart Mowrer, *The Crisis in Psychiatry and Religion* (Princeton: Van Nostrand, 1961), pp. 149 ff.

30. Freud, *GIP*, pp. 25 ff; *BPP*, pp. 47 ff.

31. Freud, *BPP, pp.* 40-41.

32. Hiltner, *Religion and Health, op. cit.*, p. 23, says that the distinction between healing and salvation is that healing belongs to the world of time and salvation to the world of eternity. Tillich, *RRH*, p. 356, points out that Hiltner's view ignores the cosmic and universal character of illness and healing, of fall into sin and of salvation: "It does not see that the eternal fulfillment is actual in the fragmentary fulfillment in time and space. Healing as well as salvation are temporal, and, at the same time, are eternal . . . From this point of view, it becomes impossible for the physician to relegate salvation to a fantastic realm of the eternal, and likewise impossible for the minister to deprive the physician's work, even when religion is not explicitly used in it, of its absolute seriousness." Hiltner

has in his later works come closer to Tillich's view. See Hiltner, *Preface to Pastoral Theology* (New York: Abingdon, 1958), pp. 89 ff.

33. Booth, *PSF,* describes the crisis in the understanding of human behavior in natural sciences in the following way: "It has become more and more difficult to find in their systems a place which accounted in a consistently rational manner for the fact that new forms of life have appeared on earth, that people have been moved by the spirit to think new thoughts and to decide on a new way of life. In Darwinistic tradition the explanation became chance, which became the prime mover of evolution with natural laws as its subsidiaries. This is an extreme of the logical impasse of determination." Cf. Harold Kelman, "Psychiatry and Existentialism," in Leon Salzman and Jules H. Masserman (eds.), *Modern Concepts of Psychoanalysis* (New York: Philosophical Library, 1962), pp. 120 ff.

34. C. G. Jung, "Answer to Job," *Collected Works* (New York: Pantheon, 1958), XI, 360, makes a distinction between physical and psychic realities. Jung states that if a group of people believes that the Rhine runs in the opposite direction from its actual one, this belief is a psychic fact, although from the physical point of view it is meaningless. On the same page, he asserts that religious statements are of this character. This kind of view results in a separation of the word from history. Jung strongly defends the dogma of the assumption of Mary and criticizes Protestantism for an unpsychological attitude. The Pope is wise when he follows the development in the psychic sphere. Jung argues that a process which has been latent almost two thousand years has now reached a point where a new, more crystallized image of God emerges. The Pope is right when he confirms it without paying attention to the criticism of the natural sciences, because the psychic processes in which religion becomes realized follow their own laws (p. 465).

35. Harold G. Wolff, "The Mind-Body Relationship," *Journal of Religion and Health,* I, No. 1 (1961), pp. 17-18, "Mind resides in every cell of the body . . . Mind is the organism."

36. Booth, *PSF,* describes the break-through of this view by saying that the functioning of consciousness was earlier considered to be only a part of the physiology of the brain, as though different parts of the brain function in different processes of mind. Three scientists have now seriously questioned this kind of interpretation: Sherrington, a physiologist; von Weizsäcker, a neurologist; and Schrödinger, a physicist. All three have come by different ways to the same conclusion that consciousness is a primary phenomenon of existence. It is not possible to locate the conscious life of man in any special part of the body, although it is possible to cause disturbances in the conscious life by damaging the brain or by removing physical stimulation from the body. Cf. C. S. Sherrington, *Man on His Nature* (New York: Macmillan, 1941); Viktor von Weizsäcker, *Der*

Gestaltkreis (Stuttgart, 1950); and Erwin Schrödinger, *What is Life?* (Cambridge, Eng.: University, 1951).

37. Cf. Bonhoeffer, *SC*, p. 42: "Only in an interaction with other spirits is a self-conscious thinking and willing possible and meaningful. It is above all the social phenomenon, language, which is so close to thinking that it makes thinking possible. Language comes before thinking; the word before spirit." He adds, "There is no experience of 'Thou' without an 'I'; the other is not known in epistemological categories" (p. 48).

5. *The Communal Nature of Illness*

38. Booth, *PSF*: "In reality the action of the organism on the environment is simultaneous with the action of the environment on the organism . . . In each decision the individual and the environment are both active and passive; the decisions take place not in the individual, but between two individuals or between the individual and a larger environment . . . Thus a close analogy exists between the outcome of a friendly or hostile engagement between two individuals and the way different allied and conflicting motivations evolve into a decision within one individual." See also Booth, "Variety in Personality and Its Relation to Health," *Review of Religion*, X (1946), 388 ff.

Cf. Daniel Day Williams, *op. cit.*, p. 26, who analyzes the significance of this kind of view for theology: "What has to be recognized is the significance of the fact that every part of his being and his experience is linked actually or potentially with every other part . . . But once we have grasped the principle of linkage we see how meaningless a sharp distinction between therapy and salvation becomes." Williams has been influenced in his theology by Whitehead.

Cf. Alfred North Whitehead, *Modes of Thought* (New York: Macmillan, 1938), p. 96: "Thus as disclosed in the fundamental essence of our experience, the togetherness of things involves some doctrine of mutual immanence. In some sense or other, this community of the actualities of the world means that each happening is a factor in the nature of every other happening . . . Thus each occasion, although engaged in its own immediate self-realization, is concerned with the universe." This viewpoint is also emphasized strongly in the writings of Charles Williams, who speaks of "co-inherent" life; see his *Selected Writings* (London: University, 1961), pp. 112-31.

39. These problems were at the center of the discussions between psychiatrists and theologians at the Church Institute in Järvenpää, Finland, in the years 1954 to 1960. See Aarne Siirala, "The Meaning of Illness," *op. cit.*, pp. 153 ff. One result of these discussions and conferences was the establishment of the Therapeia-Foundation for the promotion of sociopathological research.

40. Martti Siirala, *op. cit.,* pp. 38-93; Freud, "A Preface," *op. cit.,* pp. 43 ff.

41. Martti Siirala, *op. cit.,* pp. 14, 182 ff.; Aarne and Martti Siirala, *Elämän Ykseys* ("The Oneness of Life") (Helsinki: WSOY, 1960), pp. 51-74.

42. Wilhelm Kütemeyer, "Einleitung," in Martti Siirala, *op. cit.,* pp. 12 ff., describes a conference (*Symposium für Psychotherapie der Schizophrenie,* Zurich, 1959) at which he asked Professor Bally why our culture has taken such a deep interest in the encounter with the mentally ill in our midst. Kütemeyer continues: "He referred to the loss of identity of the person which seems to be one of the basic characteristics of our society. The urgent attempt to reach a therapy of schizophrenia in our days is to try, from the midst of a desperate state of society in its tendency toward schizophrenia, to go to the depths of the statement, in any case with the individual."

43. René A. Spitz, "Hospitalism," in Ruth S. Eissler *et al.* (eds.), *Psychoanalytic Study of the Child* (New York: Int. Univs., 1945), I, 52-74. Cf. Booth, *RFP.*

44. Viktor E. Frankl, *From Death Camp to Existentialism* (Boston: Beacon, 1959) and "Psychiatry and Man's Quest for Meaning," *Journal of Religion and Health,* I, No. 2 (1962), 93 ff.

45. Goldstein, *op. cit.,* pp. 82-83.

46. *Ibid.,* pp. 140-41.

47. Goldstein aims to show that the theory according to which human behavior is determined by certain drives and instincts is based on observations made in situations where some organic functions have been isolated from others. Under such conditions the functions in question become pathological. In the experiments on which the instinct theory is based, use has been made of either animals or children who do not yet have a strongly developed center in their organism, a center which should hold the organism together as a whole. The theory of special, isolated instincts becomes unnecessary if the instinctual functions of the human organism are viewed as forms in which the organism expresses itself as a totality (*ibid.,* p. 144).

48. Booth, "Values in Nature and in Psychotherapy," *Archives of General Psychiatry,* VIII (1963), 32. This thought has been presented by D. Rioch in the article "Research Techniques in Schizophrenia" in Lilly's book *Mental Effects of Reduction Ordinary Levels of Physical Stimuli on Intact, Healthy Persons* ("Psychiatric Research Reports 5"; Washington, 1956). Cf. Martti Kaila and Hans Buerger-Prinz, "On the Structure of the Amnestic Syndrome," in David Rapaport (ed.), *Organization and Pathology of Thought* (New York: Columbia Univ., 1959), pp. 650-89. Rapaport says of the views of Kaila: "The evidence advanced by Buerger-

Prinz and Kaila . . . suggests that thought pathology always involves all aspects of the thought process. . ." (*ibid.*, p. 720).

49. Booth, *RFP*, pp. 52 ff. A pathologist describes the cancer cell in the following way: "The cancer cells act as if they were antisocial, though not in the sense of wishing to destroy the healthy tissues, but just not caring what happens as long they survive. They appear unmoral rather than immoral"; Lerner, in *The Urologic and Cutaneous Review*, LI, (1947), 688.

Booth writes in his study *Lung Cancer and Personality*, to be published in the near future: "The environmental factor in the pathogenesis of cancer is represented by the loss of an important object relationship (Le Shan etc., *"Loss of cathexes as a common psychodynamic characteristic of cancer patients,"* Psychol. Reports 2:183, 1956) . . . cancer develops in the organ which is particularly involved in the disturbed object relationship, e.g. in the breast, the cervix and the prostate. The latter, for instance, occurs far more often in cultural groups in which love making is not carried out to the point of full sexual intercourse, similarly breast cancer occurs far more frequently in cultural and economic groups in which mothers do not breast-feed their children. It seems that such early disturbances of the biological object create an organ fixation point. One may think of a cancer *in situ*. The latter becomes activated when in a later phase of life an important object is lost which is symbolically related to the traumatized organ, e.g., breast cancer when the independence of grown-up children makes psychological mothering impossible."

50. It has been stated, e.g., that there is a higher incidence of lung cancer in immigrants who have come from the industrial areas of England to South Africa, than in the white natives of South Africa. See Dean, "Lung Cancer Among White South Africans," *British Medical Journal*, No. 31 (1959).

51. Jose Angel Bustamante, "The Importance of Cultural Factors in Mental Hygiene," *International Journal of Social Psychiatry*, Vol. VI (1960), Nos. 3-4., uses research results which show that the analysis of cultures cannot be ignored in the study of mental illnesses: (1) There is almost no schizophrenia in illiterate communities (Faris and Devereaux, "Some Observations on the Incidence of Schizophrenia in Primitive Societies," *Journal of Abnormal and Social Psychology*, 1934). (2) In New Guinea there is schizophrenia among illiterates only among those who have been in contact with Europeans (C. J. Seligman). (3) Among the natives of the Canary Islands there are no suicides (L. Dublin, R. Bunzel). (4) Manic-depressive psychosis is very common, e.g., in Denmark, but extremely rare among African Negroes (E. Wittkower, J. Fried).

52. Richter, "The Phenomenon of Sudden Unexplained Death in Animals and Men," in Herman Feifel (ed.), *The Meaning of Death* (New York: McGraw-Hill, 1959).

53. Paul E. Pfuetze, "The Concept of the Self in Contemporary Psychotherapy," *Pastoral Psychology*, No. 2 (1958), p. 10; Anselm Strauss (ed.), *The Social Psychology of George Herbert Mead* (Chicago: University, 1956). See the presentation by Munroe, *op. cit.*, pp. 333 ff., of the significance of Adler and his school of thought in the history of psychoanalysis. Rudolf Dreikurs, "Adlerian Psychotherapy," in Moreno (ed.), *op. cit.*, I, 111 ff., describes the Adlerian view as follows: Man is an indivisible social being who establishes goals and tries to reach them. As a social being man is motivated by the will to be integrated in society and by the desire to be accepted by it. Only in a group is man able to realize himself. The most basic decisions in human existence are made in the relationship of the individual to society. The decisive factor in the illness of man is his feeling of inadequacy or unworthiness stemming from his failure to find his place in society. Therapy has the task of educating the sick to find a new personal integration with society.

54. Buber, *WAWL*. Cf. Bonhoeffer, *SC*, p. 45, "The entire spirituality of man is intertwined with society and is built upon the basic relationship of Me and Thee." Pfuetze, *op. cit.*, p. 13, points out that it was Freud's experience of the importance and meaningfulness of interpersonal reality which drove him to reject the use of hypnosis. Although Freud did not immediately realize the importance of his discovery, when he later developed his theory of the super-ego he paid earnest attention to the social character of the ego.

55. Buber, *Between Man and Man* (Boston: Beacon, 1955), pp. 31-32: "Community is where community happens. Collectivity is based on an organized atrophy of personal existence, community on its increase and confirmation in life lived towards one another. The modern zeal for collectivity is a flight from community's testing and consecration of the person, a flight from the vital dialogic . . ." Professor P. Ricoeur of the Sorbonne in a lecture at Union Theological Seminary, New York, 1961, expressed the thought that the theory of Marx has often been one-sidely characterized as collective and materialistic. In its essence, according to Ricoeur, the theory of Marx is a humanistic philosophy of man, who has become estranged from his essential being. Marx aims to show that man is able to destroy himself through the institutions he creates, that the perversion of man is expressed in the very historical structures in which he tries to realize himself; man can lose his humanity in the collective structures of life. Cf. Tillich, *PE*, p. 279, "Christianity and Marxism agree that the nature of man cannot be determined from above history, that man's historical existence is decisive for every doctrine of man. And they agree that the nature of man cannot be determined by the characteristics of the individual man . . . Perdition and salvation are universal and historical."

56. Buber, *WAWL*, p. 105.

57. Hans Zetterberg (ed.), *Sociology in the United States of America* (Paris: UNESCO, 1957), in his general presentation of American sociological research mentions studies of the reality of illness in a separate section at the very end of his book. In the chapter which deals with social institutions there are studies of the court of justice, the military establishment, educational institutions, science, industry, religion, family, and vocations, but hospitals are not even mentioned.

58. Abbot P. Herman, *Approach to Social Problems* (Boston: Ginn, 1949), pp. 7 ff.

59. Rieff states in his paper "*A Schema of Therapeutic Types*" presented at the 1961 meeting of the American Psychological Association: "From Plato and Aristotle, through Burke and Tocqueville, the therapeutic implication of social theory is remarkably consistent: an individual can exercise his gifts and powers fully only by participating in the common life. This is the classical ideal. The healthy man is in fact the good citizen. Thus was the therapeutic and the moral connected in the Western tradition of social theory. In the Middle Ages, this tradition was institutionalized in a church civilization, with the therapeutic functions reserved to professionals within the churches. On the symbolic level, the integrative functions were expressed in such doctrines as that of natural law. Wherever classical social theory is asked, "What cures?" always and everywhere the final answer is that the community cures. The function of the therapist is to commit the patient to the symbol system of the community . . ."

60. Talcott Parsons, "A Sociological Approach," in *Religion, Culture and Health* (New York: New York Univ., 1961), pp. 3-6.

61. In the article "Society as Patient," *American Journal of Sociology,* Vol. XLII (1936), No. 3 (copyright 1936 by The University of Chicago), Lawrence Frank says of social problems (p. 335), ". . . we can view all of them as different symptoms of the same disease," and adds (p. 337): "At the present we cherish a belief in a normal intact society against which we see these criminals, these psychopaths, these warring husbands and wives, these recalcitrant adolescents, these shameless prostitutes . . . This assumption of individual depravity or perversity gives us a comfortable feeling that all is well socially, but that certain individuals are outrageously violating the laws and customs that all decent people uphold . . . It is, indeed, interesting to see how this conception of a social norm, with individuals as violators and frustrators of normality, runs through so much of our thinking." Cf. Herman, *op. cit.,* pp. 13 and 21, who states that the immense development in social sciences during recent decades at first aroused optimism concerning the possibilities of building a preventive social work through the social sciences. Many educational, psychiatric and marriage counseling centers developed. According to the opinion of experts, Herman states, these centers have not changed the course of development as ex-

pected. Herman asks whether these disappointments are not partly due to the fact that the problems have been met separately; since the work of the centers has not been integrated and the problems have been encountered as isolated phenomena.

62. John Gillin, "Cross-Cultural Aspects of Socio-Cultural Therapy," in Moreno (ed.), *op. cit.*, II, 224-30. See also *Psychiatry*, XI (1948), 387-400. Another classical example is the description by Rasmussen in Lessa and Vogt, *op. cit.*, pp. 362-67, of the therapeutic methods of the Eskimos (*iglulik*). Cf. Honko, "Varhaiskantaiset . . .," *op. cit.*, pp. 64-66: "The presentation by Rasmussen has become classical . . . He tells how an iglulik-shaman cured an almost totally paralyzed woman when the people of the village were present . . . Most remarkable in that description is that the community felt collective responsibility for the tabu-transgression; the healer himself also asks whether he or his wife had transgressed some rule. It is obvious that the readiness to confess and the humble asking for forgiveness was not limited only to the patient; the whole community has to show the same readiness and obedience. Both the healer and the audience confess indirectly that they are guilty of transgressions of values; they take the patient's situation as their own and defend it. The healer performs the interview as accurately as possible so that perfect purity can be reached; the audience helps in confession and acts through intercession."

63. Ackerknecht, *op. cit.*, p. 351, states that a therapist in a primitive culture has at his command stronger means than a modern psychotherapist because he is not limited to acting with the powers of only his own personality. In his person is incarnated the beliefs of the whole community: "His rite is part of the common faith of the whole community which not seldom assists *in corpore* at his healing act or even participates in singing and dancing. The whole weight of the tribe's religion, myths, history, and community spirit enters into the treatment."

64. Cf. Honko, "Varhaiskantaiset . . .," *op. cit.*, p. 55, who states that studies in primitive medicine show how central is the role of the community in those cultures; the community creates norms for man's attitudes. Primitive therapeutic methods are basically social institutions. The performance of the healing rite looks like the performance of a well rehearsed play (p. 57). Cf. also Honko, *Krankheitsprojektile* (Helsinki, 1959). Köngäs states in her presentation of Honko's studies: "At the end of the study Honko establishes what he calls *das Idealschema des Heilungsaktes*, the ideal scheme of the cure. If this scheme is applicable, we are dealing with the start of structural analysis of nonverbal folklore" (*The Slavic and East European Journal*, V, No. 4 (1960), 389-90).

65. Gillin, *op. cit.*, p. 227, also presents interesting information about the personality structure of these healers. All of them received the call to their task in dreams, and they all tried to avoid and escape the call. They were obedient only after long inner resistance. Gillin presents the hypoth-

esis that all the healers have suffered from serious mental disease. It is obvious, Gillin states, that the community of San Luis uses its schizophrenics as healers.

66. E. E. Krapf, "The Concept of Social Psychiatry," *International Journal of Social Psychiatry*, Vol. VI (1960), Nos. 1-20. J. L. Halliday, *Psychosocial Medicine: A Study of the Sick Society* (New York: Norton, 1948) defines social psychiatry differently, stating that its goal is to diagnose and to treat the sick community. See also Dunham, "Current Status of Ecological Research in Mental disorder," *Social Forces*, No. 25 (1948) and Hollingshead *et. al.*, "Social Mobility and Mental Illness," *American Sociological Review*, No. 19 (1954).

67. Krapf, *op. cit.*, emphasizes in his analysis of the statement of the committee of experts that the object of psychiatric study and treatment is the disturbed individual. One has to hold on to the basic epistemological principle, Krapf continues, that psychological study can never lead to a full understanding of the objective spirit.

68. Kütemeyer's book on the illness of Europe, *Die Krankheit Europas* (Berlin: Scherkamp Verlag, 1951), contains a profound analysis of those tendencies in our culture which have led to the "concentration" of demonic powers. Cf. Kütemeyer, "Einleitung," *op. cit.*, p. 18, "The development of social pathology is a necessary consequence of the treatment of individual sicknesses." See also Jean Carol, *Lazarus unter uns* (Stuttgart, 1959).

69. Aarne and Martti Siirala, *op. cit.*, pp. 75 ff., analyze this phenomenon in an article "Common perversion—Whose responsibility?," dealing with the material of the Nuremberg trials. Tillich says that in the history of the attitudes of Germans toward the Jews one can see the struggle of the German people with the prophetic tradition.—"Our analysis of the structure of the religious, especially of the polarity of the sacramental and the prophetic, makes it possible to answer the basic question of the topic of this lecture. Above all we are able to state what is the function of the Jewish people in known history. It is to keep alive the spirit of prophecy toward themselves, toward national groups, and toward the Christian churches, whenever they become prisoners of space. The Jews are and will be the people of time"; *Die Judenfrage, ein christliches und ein deutsches Problem* ("Schriftenreihe der deutschen Hochschule für Politik; Berlin, 1953).

70. Martti Siirala, *op. cit.*, pp. 39-65.

71. *Ibid.*, pp. 66-72.

72. Kütemeyer, "Einleitung," *op. cit.*, p. 14: "The difficult confrontation of forces which cannot be united, which are intermingled in the sick person in a labyrinthine way, can begin to be solved when the forces are transferred to the physician. When they are taken over by another, so that one suffers for another, these forces lose their pathological, destructive character, and bring healing not only to the sick person but to the physician as well."

73. Martti Siirala, *op. cit.,* p. 90, "Fellow men participate in the phenomenon of the sickness itself. They play their roles inside the sickness."

74. Aarne and Martti Siirala, *op. cit.,* p. 67; Martti Siirala, *op. cit.,* p. 227, "In taking upon himself our burdens the schizophrenic embodies our basic splits; in him they become a manifest predicament."

75. Goldstein, *op. cit.,* p. 123; cf. Bonhoeffer, *SC,* pp. 68 ff., who states that sociology has refused to accept the concept of a community organism as a personal reality because its thinking has been dominated by a wrong concept of the human organism. Cf. Whitehead, *op. cit.,* pp. 95-96: ". . . the world for me is nothing else than how the functionings of my body present it for my experience . . . Knowledge of the world is nothing else than an analysis of the functionings. And yet, on the other hand, the body is merely one society of functionings within the universal society of the world. We have to construe the world in terms of the bodily society, and the bodily society in terms of the general functionings of the world."

76. Goldstein, *op. cit.,* p. 230.

6. *Healing Is Hidden in Illness*

77. Booth, "Variety in Personality . . . ," *op. cit.,* pp. 402 ff., points out that illness was formerly considered a weakness. Experience in many fields of the encounter with illness has told us, however, that precisely those parts of the organism which have developed the greatest strength are most susceptible to disease: "Disease may be considered the punishment for having favored one's strongest function and neglected the weaker ones" (p. 404); "Sickness assails the function of the personality which has been used most particularly in meeting the demands of society" (p. 402).

78. Freud and Breuer, *op. cit.,* p. 115.

79. *Ibid.,* pp. 117-18.

80. Friberg states in a criticism of two books which deal with psychoanalysis, in the *Partisan Review,* No. 1 (1961), that studies in psychoanalysis often have too little to do with the original sources. In such studies one can still meet the view that repression should involve the extinction of instincts through a realization of more spiritual needs. Cf. Arvid Runestam, *Psychoanalysis and Christianity* (Rock Island, Ill.: Augustana, 1958), p. 32, who says that Freud's concept of repression means that neuroses are caused by the conflict between the moral standards of society and the instinctual life of man: "The modern civilized community with its mores and morality has set up too high a standard for a released expression of the instincts and has restrained a free functioning of the libido . . ." According to Runestam this would be the Freudian view of the present situation of man. Since Runestam's book is dominated by this erroneous interpretation, it contains discussion only of those psychological schools of thought which are similarly based on a wrong interpretation of Freud's concept of repression. Runestam

also expresses his theological standpoint in these categories and states that the "Christian" solution differs from the psychoanalytic one in its understanding of morality: "The fault has not been that the moral force has been too strong, so that it has not permitted the drift life to exercise its rightful function; rather the fault is that it has been too weak" (p. 58).

81. Freud and Breuer, *op. cit.*, p. 119. In this connection Freud seems to understand illness as an escape from anxiety. Such an escape led Elizabeth to a point where unconscious mechanisms took command. When the patient allows the anxiety to come into his consciousness, possibilities for recovery are opened. Freud emphasizes the difference among fright, fear, and anxiety. Anxiety is a state in which one prepares for an expected danger, although the character of the danger is still unknown. Fear always has some object. Fright is that state in which one finds that he is in danger without being prepared for it. When Freud analyzes the character of traumatic neuroses he says that anxiety does not produce them; rather anxiety protects man from fright and from the neuroses connected with it. See Freud, *BPP*, pp. 29-30.

7. *Man's Urge for Death and Life*

82. The quotations that follow are from the English Translation of Freud's *Beyond the Pleasure Principle (BPP)*.

83. von Weizsäcker, *Pathosophie* (Göttingen: Vandenhoeck und Ruprecht, 1956), p. 9.

84. Booth, "Disease as Message," *Journal of Religion and Health*, I, (1962), 309-18.

85. Freud, *BPP*, p. 21.

86. Fechner (*Einige Ideen zur Schöpfungs—und Entwicklungsgeschichte der Organismen*, 1873) had already presented a theory concerning the relationship between the feeling of pleasure or pain and the variation in states of equilibrium or inequilibrium which can be observed in the organism. According to Fechner's hypothesis, every psycho-physic movement which comes to consciousness brings pleasure when the organism gets a better equilibrium, but causes pain when balance is lost. Cf. Freud, *BPP*, p. 23.

87. A good survey of the theories of different psychoanalytic schools concerning psychodynamics (id, ego, superego) is presented, e.g., by Munroe, *op. cit.*, pp. 82 ff., and by Martti Paloheimo, *Mielenterveys ja ihmissuhteet* ("Mental Health and Human Relations") (Helsinki: WSOY, 1958), pp. 68 ff.

88. Freud, *BPP*, pp. 28-30 and *Origins of Psychoanalysis, op. cit.*, p. 22. Cf. Munroe, *op. cit.*, p. 80: "Since all living things arose out of the inanimate, the trend toward death may be considered inborn, a death instinct, *thanatos*. The striving here is no longer for a 'pleasurable' reduction of tension among organ systems which constantly build up new energies. The

striving of the death instinct is toward absolute zero. Freud accepted for this process a term suggested by an early follower . . . the Nirvana principle."

89. Freud can characterize this compulsion to repeat as demonic (*BPP*, pp. 40 ff.).

90. *Ibid.*, p. 45.

91. *Ibid.*, p. 67.

92. *Ibid.*, p. 71.

93. Freud, *Origins of Psychoanalysis, op. cit.*, p. 22; cf. Munroe, *op. cit.*, pp. 80 ff.

94. Freud, *BPP*, p. 72.

95. *Ibid.*, p. 76.

96. *Ibid.*, pp. 73-74.

97. *Ibid.*, p. 80.

98. *Ibid.*, p. 81.

99. *Ibid.*, p. 89; cf. Freud, *Origins of Psychoanalysis, op. cit.*, p. 20. Freud, *BPP*, p. 100, makes reference, although hesitantly, to the mythological view of the origin of the sexual instinct, as expressed by Plato through Aristophanes in the *Symposium*. According to that view, human nature was supposed to have been totally different originally from what it had become. There had once been three sexes: male, female, and a sex which united the two. There had been two of each of the vital organs in every man. Zeus decided then to divide man in two, each half continuing to desire his other half. This myth is important because it describes the force which arouses instincts as a need to return to an earlier state. Freud states at the end of his presentation that the pleasure principle seems actually to serve the death instinct. Cf. Munroe, *op. cit.*, p. 80, "Eros came to represent all the trends in the organism which seek to unify, bind together, preserve and build up."

8. *Illness as a Stumbling Block*

100. Munroe, *op. cit.*, pp. 108-10.

101. Karen Horney, *Neurosis and Human Growth* (New York: Norton, 1950), emphasizes strongly that human nature is not in any respect structurally destructive. There is in the depths of the human personality a dynamic and constructive principle, "the real self." Cf. Bromberg, *op. cit.*, pp. 220 ff.

102. Booth, *RFP*, pp. 55-56.

103. *Ibid.*, p. 56.

104. The thought that every organism seeks its own special way to be sick and to die has been developed especially by L. Szondi, *Schicksalanalyse* (Basel: Benno Schwabe, 1944). Cf. Booth, *RFP*, p. 56.

105. Booth, "Disease as Message," *op. cit.*, points out that absurdities result if sexuality or the destructive instincts are understood as abstract forces. Booth emphasizes that nature is a unique and concrete process in which all units are always in reciprocal interdependence. Every single unit is a part of the whole process; nothing can be abstracted as an isolated force or factor.

106. Shaw, *The Doctor's Dilemma* (London, 1911). Cf. Booth, "Disease as Message," *op. cit.*

107. Booth, *PSF.* The biologists have also raised warnings against the kind of encounter with illness which creates in the general public aspirations of a final victory over illness. One of the biologists associated with the Rockefeller Institute, R. J. Dubos, has published a book with the telling title *The Mirage of Health* (New York: Harper's, 1959).

108. Booth, *PSF,* points out that one can differentiate between subject and object only by limiting the analysis to certain phenomena. The relationship between subject and object is not determined by physical factors but by the direction of the intentions of the subject. When something is objectivated, e.g., in physics or in biology, with some special scientific purpose in mind, the influences of that object are determinants for the physicists or the biologist according to the substance and structure of the object. As for the content of consciousness the influence of the object is entirely determined by what it means for the subject. Consciousness is not an object.

9. *Therapy Leads to Prophetic Questions*

109. Freud, *BPP*, p. 22; *GIP*, pp. 24ff.

110. Freud, *BPP*, p. 38.

111. *Ibid.*, p. 76.

112. Freud, *GIP*, p. 25.

113. Freud, *BPP*, p. 93, states that Jung has escaped from the dualism between the life and death instincts into a monistic view. Cf. Glover, *op. cit.*, p. 57, "Jung embraced with . . . enthusiastic haste a monistic theory of mental energy."

114. Freud, *BPP*, p. 105.

115. *Ibid.*, p. 110; Freud, *The Future of an Illusion* (New York: Liveright, 1953), p. 2.

116. Max Scheler, *Die Stellung des Menschen im Kosmos* (Darmstadt, 1928). See Goldstein, *op. cit.*, p. 8.

CHAPTER 4. THERAPY AND PROPHECY

1. *History as Therapy and Prophecy*

1. P. A. Heiberg (ed.), *Søren Kierkegaard's efterladte Papirer* (Copenhagen, 1926), IX, 75.

2. Erikson, *op. cit.*

3. *Ibid.*, pp. 13-14. Kierkegaard claims that Luther overemphasized this subjective patienthood without reaching the perspective of the physician, *Laegens overskuelse.*

4. Harold Kelman, "Clinical Psychoanalytic Concepts of the Etiology of the Neuroses," paper read at a symposium of the Society of Medical Psychoanalysis, March 16-17, 1962, New York, and "Life History as Therapy," I-III, *American Journal of Psychoanalysis*, Vol. XV (1955), No. 2; Vol. XVI (1956), Nos. 1-2.

5. Tillich, *PE*, pp. 37ff., Norman O. Brown, *Life Against Death: The Psychoanalytical Meaning of History* (Middletown, Conn.: Wesleyan Univ., 1959), p. 15, writes: "But if historians have failed to follow Freud, poets have characteristically anticipated him. Is there not, for example, a still unexplored truth in the statement of the German poet Hebbel: 'Is it hard to recognize that the German nation has up till now no life history to show for itself, but only the history of a disease (*Krankheitsgeschichte*).'" Cf. Riese, *CD*, p. 86, who points out that the histories of disease, grown in the Hippocratic tradition, have had an impact on the methods of Greek historiography: "The historian Thucydides was believed to have obtained instruction in methods of historical research from the physician Hippocrates."

6. Erikson, *op. cit.*, p. 14: "I have called the major crisis of adolescence the identity crisis; it occurs in that period of the life cycle when each youth must forge for himself some central perspective and direction, some working unity, out of the remnants of his childhood and the hopes of his anticipated adulthood; he must detect some meaningful resemblance between what he has come to see in himself and what his sharpened awareness tells him others judge and expect him to be." Cf. Earl A. Loomis, *The Self in Pilgrimage* (New York: Harper, 1960).

7. Erikson, *op. cit.*, p. 17.

8. *Ibid.*, p. 15.

9. *Ibid.*, p. 18, "I mean by it a habit of thinking which reduces every human situation to an analogy with an earlier one, and most of all to that earliest, simplest, and most infantile precursor, which is assumed to be its 'origin.'"

10. R. G. Collingwood, *The Idea of History* (New York, 1956), p. 226.

11. See chapter 1, note 6.

12. Erikson, *op. cit.*, p. 19, "We must grudgingly admit that even as we were trying to devise, with scientific determinism, a therapy for the few, we were led to promote an ethical disease among the many." Cf. Martti Siirala, *op. cit.*, p. 91.

13. Erikson, *op. cit.*, p. 18: Schools of thought in psychoanalysis usually follow various ideological movements, and "Maybe, then, a clinical science of the human mind will eventually demand a special historical self-awareness on the part of the clinical worker and scholar."

14. Anna Freud, *The Ego and the Mechanisms of Defense* (New York: Int. Univs., 1946), p. 177; cf.: Erikson, *op. cit.*, p. 19.

15. Erikson, *op. cit.*, p. 20.

16. Joseph Sittler, *The Ecology of Faith: The New Situation in Preaching* (Philadelphia: Muhlenberg, 1961).

17. *Ibid.*, p. 3.

18. *Ibid.*, pp. 3-5.

19. This may mean that biblical historiography challenges us in a new way. The biblical writing of history binds together in a great drama the most varied experiences in the lives of individuals and communities. It is dominated throughout by a proclamation of the history of salvation in the midst of corruption. Both the old dying mankind in Adam and the new mankind being born in Christ are community organisms—bodies which extend in time and in space over the eras of time and over the whole universe.

20. Cf. Bonhoeffer, *SC*, p. 67.

21. Etiology, of course, means a theory or a study of the causes of a phenomenon.

22. Kelman, "Clinical Psychoanalytic Concepts . . . ," *op. cit.*, p. 10, and "Life History as Therapy," *op. cit.* Cf. Walther Riese, "The Pre-Freudian Origins of Psychoanalysis," in Jules H. Masserman (ed.), *Science and Psychoanalysis* (New York, 1960), I, 47, "Should it thus be true that the natural history of neuroses merges into history of the patient's entire life, one expects to discover among the disease shaping factors no more but also no less than all factors shaping human existence." Brown, *op. cit.*, p. 12, "Freud not only maintains that human history can be understood only as a neurosis but also that the neurosis of individuals can be understood only in the context of human history as a whole . . . mankind is prisoner of the past in the same sense as 'our hysterical patients are suffering from reminiscences' and 'neurotics cannot escape from the past.'" Cf. also Rieff, "The Meaning of History and Religion in Freud's Thought," *Journal of Religion*, XXXI (1951).

23. Tillich, *TC*, pp. 31-32.

24. Brown, *op. cit.*, p. 13: "In *The Future of an Illusion,* Freud does speak of religion as a 'substitute gratification'—the Freudian analogue to the Marxian formula 'opiate of the people.' But according to the whole doctrine of repression, 'substitute gratifications'—a term which applies not only to poetry and religion but also to dreams and neurotic symptoms—contain truth: they are expressions, distorted by repression, of the immortal desires of the human heart."

25. Brown, *op. cit.,* p. 13, "Psychoanalysis must view religion both as neurosis and as that attempt to become conscious and to cure inside the neurosis itself, on which Freud came at the end of his life to pin his hopes for therapy."

26. Karl Marx, *Der Historische Materialismus* (Leipzig, 1932), p. 264. This sentence of Marx is in the same context in which he speaks of religion as the opiate of the people. Cf. Brown, *op. cit.,* p. 13.

27. Tillich, *TC,* p. 33.

28. *Ibid.,* pp. 30-31; cf. Brown, *op. cit.,* p. 93: "Repression and repetition-compulsion generate historical time. Repression transforms the timeless instinctual compulsion to repeat into the forward-moving dialectic of neurosis which is history."

29. Tillich, *TC,* p. 34; cf. the words of Oscar Cullmann on pp. 52-53 of *Christ and Time, op. cit.,* (quoted by permission): "For the Greeks, the idea that redemption is to take place through divine action in the course of events in time is impossible. . . . In the Primitive Christian preaching, on the contrary, salvation, in keeping with the Bible's linear understanding of time, is conceived strictly in terms of a time process."

30. There are also strong tendencies in current therapeutic movements to seek contact with contemporary mystical trends, especially with the mystical religions of the East. See Kelman, "Communing and Relating," *op. cit.*

31. Tillich, *TC,* pp. 34-35.

32. Brown, *op. cit.,* p. 86.

33. Erikson, *op. cit.,* p. 20.

34. *Ibid.,* pp. 25-26, mentions the German theologian Scheel as a typical representative of Protestant theology in this respect. According to Erikson, Scheel explains all of Luther's attacks of unconsciousness, of deep anxiety, of hallucinations, of despair, as immediately caused by God. Scheel views all these attacks as "heavenly," *Katastrophen von Gottes Gnaden.* Erikson views the interpretation of Luther given by the Roman Catholic theologian Denifle as structurally similar, although it is opposite in content. According to this theory, everything in Luther's life was caused by the devil. Common to both interpretations is explaining the various phases in Luther's life without reference to psychological motivations.

35. *Ibid.,* p. 251.

36. When we analyzed the history of the encounter with illness in the light of therapy, we observed that when the naturalistic tendency dominates, illness as a psychological reality is avoided. This same tendency has also caused other unhistorical attitudes toward history. See Tillich, *PE,* p. 23.

37. Cf. Brown, *op. cit.,* p. 19, ". . . the method of psychoanalytical therapy is to deepen the historical consciousness of the individual (fill up the memory gaps) till he awakens from his own history as from a nightmare . . . If historical consciousness is finally transformed into psychoanalytic consciousness, the grip of the dead hand of the past on life in the present would be loosened, and man would be ready to live instead of making history . . .". Cf. also Bonhoeffer, *Prisoner for God,* (ed. Eberhard Bethge and trans. Reginald H. Fuller (New York: Macmillan, 1954), p. 153: "Israel is redeemed out of Egypt in order to live before God on earth. The salvation myths deny history in the interests of an eternity after death. Sheol and Hades are no metaphysical theories, but images which imply that the past, while it still exists, has only a shadowy existence in the present."

38. A Roman Catholic scholar, William F. Lynch, in his analysis of the history of Western literature, *Christ and Apollo,* has attempted to show how a literary style breaks when there is a rebellion against the finite and the limited, when time is escaped. Lynch states that there seems to be in human nature a tendency to destroy time, to make it immovable or to use it for something; one should go into time, live in it. Reason tries to find a position outside the stream of time in order to avoid the confusing reality of concrete time (p. 32). This escape from time becomes at the same time an escape from dying, which alone is the narrow way to life (p. 38.) Human time is a divine structure, narrow, but powerful (p. 41). It is not proper to say that Christ redeemed time; time has never needed redemption. It needed only someone to enter it, to open its inner resources. This happened in Christ (p. 51); *Christ and Apollo: The Dimensions of the Literary Imagination* (New York: Sheed & Ward, 1960). Cf. Richard R. Niebuhr, *Resurrection and Historical Reason* (New York: Scribner's, 1957).

39. Tillich, *PE,* p. 24.

40. *Ibid.,* p. 24.

41. *Ibid.,* p. 25. The American playwright Arthur Miller has profoundly analyzed the problems connected with persecution in his play *The Crucible* (New York, 1959), which is based on the New England persecutions of witches at the end of the seventeenth century. Miller emphasizes that one central motive in the persecutions was an absolute dualism which makes an absolute knowledge of good and evil possible (pp. 30-33).

42. Buber, *GP,* p. 235.

43. *Ibid.,* p. 247.

44. *Ibid.*, p. 254.

45. *Ibid.*

46. *Ibid.*, pp. 260-61.

47. Tillich, *PE*, p. 25.

48. Cf. Aarne Siirala, *Gottes Gebot bei Martin Luther, op. cit.*, pp. 178-266.

49. Cf. Tillich, *TC*, pp. 38-39, and "Jewish Influences on Contemporary Christian Theology," *Cross Currents*, II (1952), No. 3, 38. See also Zilboorg, Psychoanalysis and Religion (New York: Farrar, Straus & Cudahy, 1962), pp. 115-16.

2. *The Prophetic Word in a Sick World*

50. Brown, *op. cit.*, pp. 215-16.

51. Luther and Freud are both increasingly recognized as central figures in the development of Western culture. In the light of the history of therapy and prophecy it is understandable that Luther has been very much ignored in the analyses of the history of ideas in Western culture. Luther seems to have been some kind of stumbling block in the history of the forming of words. See Aarne Siirala, *Gottes Gebot bei Martin Luther, op. cit.*, p. 15. Obviously the therapeutic encounter with illness has shown the relevance of Luther in a new way. This seems to be especially the case in Anglo-Saxon culture. Beside the books of Erikson and Brown this is seen in the play of John Osborne, *Luther* (London, 1961). Concerning the impact of Freud on Western culture see Nelson (ed.), *op. cit.* A play has also been written about Freud; Henry Denker, *A Far Country* (New York, 1961), as has a movie based on a manuscript by Jean-Paul Sartre.

52. Cf. Buber, *WAWL*, p. 107.

53. Erikson, *op. cit.*, p. 23.

54. *Ibid.*, p. 23.

55. *Ibid.*, p. 47.

56. *Ibid.*, p. 162.

57. *Ibid.*, p. 163.

58. Cf. J. Huizinga, *The Waning of the Middle Ages* (New York: Doubleday, 1954), p. 204; Erikson, *op. cit.*, p. 187.

59. Erikson, *op. cit.*, p. 190.

60. *Ibid.*, p. 185.

61. *Ibid.*, p. 186.

62. *Ibid.*, p. 191. Cf. Giorgio de Santillana, *The Age of Adventure* (Boston, 1957), pp. 13-14 and E. Crosirer (ed.), *The Renaissance Philosophy of Man* (Chicago, 1956), p. 225.

63. Erikson, *op. cit.*, p. 192.

64. Fromm, *Psychoanalysis and Religion* (New Haven: Yale, 1950), starts his analysis of the relationship between psychoanalysis and religion by differentiating between two kinds of religious phenomena, authoritative and humanistic. In an authoritative religiosity the attempt is made to reach grace, security, and salvation through an entire resignation of man to the authority which comes from above. Man finds peace in his feeling of inferiority and evil and in self-contempt. Humanistic religiosity, however, which according to Fromm is represented by psychoanalysis, tries to liberate in man the abilities which have become perverted. Humanistic religiosity liberates real human nature.

Booth, "Problems of Authority . . .," *op. cit.,* pp. 203-17, shows how Fromm's view leads to the same inner conflicts and controversies as the view of Renaissance humanism: "It is an old rule that people usually persecute in others what they repress in themselves. Humanism is directed against conformity and its authoritative imposition on others, supposedly by fear of punishment. This suggests that the humanist is repressing in himself a need to see everybody in his own image . . . As humanists are human too, they fall into the same aggressiveness as their opponents, trying to impose the pattern 'Basic Human nature' " (p. 210).

65. Erikson, *op. cit.,* pp. 194-95.

66. Cf. Tillich, *PE,* pp. 152-78.

67. Erikson, *op. cit.,* pp. 197-98.

68. Tillich, *PE,* p. 91.

69. Erikson, *op. cit.,* pp. 208-213.

70. *Ibid.,* pp. 211, 213; Cf. *D. Martin Luther's Werke,* Kritische Gesamtausgabe (Weimar, 1883——), hereafter referred to as *WA;* 3, 420; 3, 289; 4, 330.

71. Erikson, *op. cit.,* p. 253.

72. *Ibid.,* p. 214; Cf. *WA* 3, 529.

73. Brown, *op. cit.,* p. 209.

74. Brown's quotations are from Obendiek's book *Der Teufel bei Martin Luther* (Berlin, 1931), pp. 53-57. See Brown, *op. cit.,* pp. 211-12.

75. Obendiek, *op. cit.,* p. 187; Brown, *op. cit.,* pp. 212-13.

76. Brown, *op. cit.,* pp. 216-17.

77. *Ibid.,* pp. 217-18.

78. *Ibid.,* p. 219, mentions in this connection the study by R. H. Tawney, *Religion and the Rise of Capitalism* (New York: Harcourt, 1957).

79. Here Brown's quotations are from a study by H. Barge, *Luther und der Frühkapitalismus* (Gütersloh, 1951), pp. 37-40; see also Obendiek, *op. cit.,* p. 172.

80. Brown, *op. cit.,* p. 224; cf. Tillich, *PE,* pp. 235-59.

81. Brown's view of the relationship between psychoanalysis and religion is seldom to be found in the literature which deals with these questions. Usually the one is seen as the "savior" of the other or vice versa. See, e.g., R. S. Lee, *Freud and Christianity* (New York: Wyn, 1949).

82. Brown, *op. cit.*, pp. 232-33.

83. D. Rössler, "Psychotherapie, Theologische Beurteilung," in *Die Religion in Geschichte und Gegenwart* (Tübingen, 1961), V, 715.

84. *Ibid.*, p. 715.

85. *Ibid.*, p. 718.

86. For example, at Union Theological Seminary, New York, a special department called "The Program in Psychiatry and Religion" for research was established in 1956 for research and the development of training methods.

87. Cf. Booth, "Research in Religion and Health: The Selection of Personnel for the Clergy" (New York: Fordham University Press, 1963) and "The Psychological Examination of Candidates for the Ministry," in Hofmann (ed.), *The Ministry and Mental Health, op. cit.* See also Wayne Oates, *The Minister's Own Mental Health* (Great Neck, N. Y.: Channel, 1961).

88. In the report "Action for Mental Health" (New York, 1961) of the Joint Commission on Mental Illness and Health which was established by the Congress of the United States in 1955, it is stated that the work of the ministry is organized in such a way that ministers have very little time for therapeutic encounter with individuals. Studies have shown that a minister uses an average of two hours a week for private counseling or individual pastoral care. Only seven per cent use more than ten hours a week for counseling. The report also says that there are too few ministers working in mental hospitals. Ministers constitute less than one half of one per cent of the total personnel of these institutions. There is one minister for every sixteen hundred patients.

89. The Academy of Religion and Mental Health in New York sponsors a regular forum in which different views of the various religious bodies meet one another. Three major groups, Jews, Roman Catholics, and Protestants, participate in the work of the Academy, which has more than three thousand individual members, of which about a third are psychiatrists. The Academy publishes a periodical *Journal of Religion and Health*. See chapter 2, note 1. Cf. I. Fred Hollander, "The Specific Nature of the Clergy's Role in Mental Health Project," *Pastoral Psychology*, November, 1959, concerning the Yeshiva University National Institute of Mental Health Project; "Religion and Mental Health: A Catholic Viewpoint," issued by the Religion and Mental Health Project, Loyola University, Chicago, published by the Academy of Religion and Mental Health; Hofmann,

"The Ministry and Mental Health," Final Report of the Harvard University Project on Religion and Mental Health to the National Institute of Mental Health (mimeographed paper of the Harvard University Project).

90. Bonhoeffer, *Prisoner for God, op. cit.*, p. 126. Behind the *Offenbarungs-positivismus* mentioned by Bonhoeffer is obviously a metaphysical concept of reality in which God is epistemologically transcendental. Revelation and the incarnation are then thought of as eternal and transcendent realities which break into the finite world. "The Word became Flesh" thus means that something abstract becomes concrete, something invisible becomes visible, something irrational becomes understandable. It is obvious that the character of Revelation and of the incarnation is seen in a different way, if this metaphysical starting point is abandoned. From the viewpoint of our theme we had rather say: "The Word became sick"; that is the meaning of the Revelation and of the incarnation. Cf. John A. T. Robinson, *The Body*: A Study in Pauline Theology (London: SCM, 1957), pp. 34-38.

91. Bonhoeffer, *Prisoner for God, op. cit.*, pp. 122-24. Cf. Freud, *Civilization and Its Discontents, op. cit.*, p. 24: "One would like to count oneself among the believers so as to admonish the philosophers who try to preserve the God of religion by substituting for him an impersonal, shadowy, abstract principle. One would like to say, 'Thou shalt not take the name of the Lord thy God in vain.' "

92. Brown, *op. cit.*, p. 71.

Epilogue

93. Bonhoeffer, *Prisoner for God, op. cit.*, pp. 142-43; 153-54; 164; 166; 173; 176.

Bibliography

ACKERKNECHT, ERWIN H. *See* LESSA.

ALLERS, RUDOLF. *Existentialism and Psychiatry*. Springfield, Ill.: Thomas, 1960.

ANDERSON, GEORGE C. "Conflicts Between Psychiatry and Religion," *Journal of the American Medical Association*, Vol. CLV (1954).

————. *Man's Right to Be Human: To Have Emotions Without Fear*. New York: Morrow, 1959.

ARIETI, SILVANO (ed.). *American Handbook of Psychiatry*. 2 vols. New York: Basic Books, 1959.

BALLY, G. "Das Diagnosenproblem in der Psychotherapie," *Der Nervenarzt*, 11 Heft (1959).

BARBU, VALER. "Psychoanalysis and Philosophy," *American Journal of Psychoanalysis*, Vol. V, No. 1 (1945).

BENEDETTI, GAETANO. "Die Welt des Schizophrenen und deren psychotherapeutische Zugänglichkeit," *Schweiz. Med. Wochenschrift*, LXXXIV (1954), 1029.

————. "Psychotherapie eines Schizophrenen," *Psyche*, Vol. IX (1955).

BIER, WILLIAM C. "Sigmund Freud and Faith," *America*, November, 1956.

BOISEN, ANTON T. *Exploration of the Inner World: A Study of Mental Disorder and Religious Experience*. New York: Harper, 1936.

————. *Out of the Depths: An Autobiographical Study of Mental Disorder and Religious Experience*. New York: Harper, 1960.

BONHOEFFER, DIETRICH. *Sanctorum Communio (SC)*. Munich: Chr. Kaiser Verlag, 1954.

————. *Prisoner for God*, ed. EBERHARD BETHGE and trans. REGINALD H. FULLER. New York: Macmillan, 1954.

BOOTH, GOTTHARD. "Conditions of Medical Responsibility," *Review of Religion*, XIII (March, 1949), 241-58.

————. "Disease as Message," *Journal of Religion and Health*, I (1962), 309-18.

————. *Lung Cancer and Personality*. Manuscript.

————. "Problems of Authority for Individual Christians: Its Use and Abuse," *Journal of Pastoral Care*, IX (1952), 203-17.

————. *Physician Between the Spirit and the Flesh (PSF)*. Manuscript.

————. "The Selection of Personnel for the Clergy," in W. C. BIER (ed.), *Research in Religion and Health*. New York: Fordham University Press, 1963.

————. "The Role of Physical Form in Psychodynamics" (*RFP*), *Psychoanalysis and the Psychoanalytical Review*, XLVII, 51-62.

————. "Values in Nature and in Psychotherapy," *Archives of General Psychiatry*, VIII (1963), 22-32.

————. "Variety in Personality and Its Relation to Health," *Review of Religion*, X (1946), 385-412.

————. *See also* MAVES; HOFMANN (ed.), *The Ministry and Mental Health*.

BOSS, MEDARD. "Daseinsanalytische Bemerkungen zu Freuds Verstellung des Unbewussten," *Zeitschrift für Psychosomatische Medizin*, January-March, 1961.

————. "Wirkungsweise und Indikation der Psychotherapie," *Schweiz.*

————. *Med. Wochenschrift*, No. 6 (1957).

BREUER, JOSEPH and FREUD, SIGMUND. *Studies in Hysteria*. Boston: Beacon, 1937.

BROMBERG, WALTER. *The Mind of Man: A History of Psychotherapy and Psychoanalysis*. New York: Harper, 1959.

BROWN, NORMAN O. *Life Against Death: The Psychoanalytical Meaning of History*. Middletown, Conn.: Wesleyan Univ., 1959.

BRUNER, JEROME S. *See* NELSON.

BUBER, MARTIN. *Between Man and Man*. Boston: Beacon, 1955.

————. *Der Glaube der Propheten* (*GP*). Zurich: Manesse Verlag, 1950. Also available in English as *The Prophetic Faith* (New York: Harper, 1960). Torchback.

————. "The William Alanson White Memorial Lectures" (*WAWL*), *Psychiatry*, Vol. XX (1957), No. 2.

BURY, J. B. *A History of Freedom of Thought*. New York: Holt, 1913.

BUSTAMANTE, JOSÉ ANGEL. "The Importance of Cultural Factors in Mental Hygiene," "*International Journal of Social Psychiatry*, Vol. VI (1960), Nos. 3-4.

CALDER, PETER RITCHIE. *Medicine and Man*. New York: New American Library, 1959. Mentor Book.

CHASE, STUART. *The Tyranny of Words*. New York: Harcourt, Brace, 1938.

CULLMAN, OSCAR. *Christ and Time*, trans. FLOYD V. FILSON. Philadelphia: Westminster, 1950.

DIEPGEN, PAUL. *Geschichte der Medizin*. 2 vols. Berlin, 1914.

DREIKURS, RUDOLF. *See* MORENO.

DUBOS, J. R. *The Mirage of Health*. New York: Harper, 1959.

EDELSTEIN, E. and L. *Asclepius: A Collection and Interpretation of the Testimonies*. Baltimore: Johns Hopkins, 1945.

EHRENWALD, JAN. *From Medicine Man to Freud.* New York: Dell, 1956.

ENTRALGO, PEDRO L. *Mind and Body. Psychosomatic Pathology: A Short History of the Evolution of Medical Thought.* New York: Kenedy, 1954.

ERIKSON, ERIK H. *Young Man Luther: A Study in Psychoanalysis and History.* New York: Norton, 1958.

FEIFEL, HERMAN (ed.). *The Meaning of Death.* New York: McGraw-Hill, 1959.

FRANK, LAWRENCE. "Society as Patient," *American Journal of Sociology,* Vol. XLII (1936), No. 3.

FRANKL, VIKTOR E. *From Death Camp to Existentialism.* Boston: Beacon, 1959.

———. *The Doctor and the Soul.* New York: Knopf, 1939.

———. "Psychiatry and Man's Quest for Meaning," *Journal of Religion and Health,* Vol. I (1962), No. 2.

FREUD, ANNA. *The Ego and the Mechanisms of Defense.* New York: Int. Univs., 1946.

FREUD, SIGMUND. *Beyond the Pleasure Principle (BPP).* New York: Liveright, 1922, and Bantam, 1959.

———. *Civilization and Its Discontents.* New York: Cape & Smith, 1930.

———. *Collected Papers.* 6 vols. London: Hogarth, 1924-1950.

———. *The Future of an Illusion.* New York: Liveright, 1953.

———. *A General Introduction to Psychoanalysis (GIP).* New York: Permabooks, 1958.

———. *The Origins of Psychoanalysis.* New York: Basic, 1954.

———. *An Outline of Psychoanalysis.* New York: Norton, 1949.

———. *See also* NELSON.

FROMM, ERICH. *Escape from Freedom.* New York: Rinehart, 1941.

———. *Man for Himself.* New York: Rinehart, 1947.

———. *Psychoanalysis and Religion.* New Haven: Yale, 1950.

———. *The Sane Society.* New York: Rinehart, 1955.

GALDSTON, IAGO (ed.). *Ministry and Medicine in Human Relations.* ("New York Academy of Medicine" Series.) New York: Int. Univs., 1955.

GILLIN, JOHN. *See* MORENO.

GLOVER, EDWARD. *Freud or Jung?* New York: Meridian, 1960.

GOLDSTEIN, KURT. *Human Nature in the Light of Psychopathology.* Cambridge: Harvard, 1951.

HALL, CALVIN S. *A Primer of Freudian Psychology.* New York: World, 1954.

HALL, CALVIN S. and LINDSEY, GARDNER. *Theories of Personality.* New York: Wiley, 1957.

HALLIDAY, J. L. *Psychosocial Medicine: A Study of the Sick Society.* New York: Norton, 1948.

202 BIBLIOGRAPHY

HARNACK, ADOLF VON. *Medizinisches aus der aeltesten Kirchengeschichte.* Leipzig: Hinrichs, 1892.

HEMPEL, JOHANNES. *Heilung als Symbol und Wirklichkeit im biblischen Schrifttum.* Göttingen: Vandenhoeck und Ruprecht, 1958.

HERMAN, ABBOT P. *Approach to Social Problems.* Boston: Ginn, 1949.

HILTNER, SEWARD. Religion and Health. New York: Macmillan, 1943.
————. *Preface to Pastoral Theology.* New York: Abingdon, 1958.

HOFMANN, HANS. *Making the Ministry Relevant.* New York: Scribner, 1960.
————. (ed.). *The Ministry and Mental Health.* New York: Association, 1960. Read especially GOTTHARD BOOTH, "The Psychological Examination of Candidates for the Ministry."
————. *Religion and Mental Health.* New York: Harper, 1961.

HONKO, LAURI. *Krankheitsprojektile.* ("Folklore Fellows' Communications" Series, No. 178.) Helsinki: Suomalaisen Tiedeakatemian julkaisusarja, 1959.
————. "Varhaiskantaiset taudinselitykset ja parantamisnäytelmä" ("Primitive Interpretations of Illness and the Healing Drama"), in Jouko Hautala (ed.), *Jumin keko.* Helsinki: Suomalaisen Kirjallisuuden Seura, 1960.

HOOK, SYDNEY (ed.). *Psychoanalysis, Scientific Method and Philosophy.* New York: New York Univ., 1959. Read especially ALEXANDER INKELES, "Psychoanalysis and Sociology."

HORNEY, KAREN. *Our Inner Conflicts: A Constructive Theory of Neurosis.* New York: Norton, 1945.
————. *Neurosis and Human Growth.* New York: Norton, 1950.

HUIZINGA, J. *The Waning of the Middle Ages.* New York: Doubleday, 1954. Anchor Book.

JONES, ERNEST. *The Life and Work of Sigmund Freud.* 3 vols. London: Hogarth, 1953-1957.
————. *The Theory of Symbolism* 5th ed. (*"Papers on Psychoanalysis"* Series.) London, 1948.

JUNG, C. G. "Answer to Job," *The Collected Works,* Vol. XI. New York: Pantheon, 1958.
————. *Psychology and Religion.* New Haven: Yale, 1938.

KAILA, MARTTI and BUERGER-PRINZ, HANS. *See* RAPAPORT.

KAPLAN, ABRAHAM. *See* NELSON.

KARDINER, ABRAM. *The Psychological Frontiers of Society.* New York: Columbia Univ., 1945.
————. *See also* NELSON.

KELLER, HELEN. *The Story of My Life.* Garden City, N. Y.: Doubleday, 1921.

KELMAN, HAROLD. "Clinical Psychoanalytic Concepts of the Etiology of the Neuroses." Paper read at a symposium of the Society of Medical Psychoanalysis, March 16-17, 1962, New York.

————. "Communing and Relating," *American Journal of Psychotherapy*, Vol. XIV (1960), No. 1.

————. " 'Kairos' and the Therapeutic Process," *Journal of Existential Psychiatry*, Vol. I (1960), No. 2.

————. "Life History as Therapy," 3 parts, *American Journal of Psychoanalysis*, Vol. XV (1955), No. 2; Vol. XVI (1956), Nos. 1-2.

————. *See also* SALZMAN and MASSERMAN.

KRAPF, E. E. "The Concept of Social Psychiatry," *International Journal of Social Psychiatry*, Vol. VI (1960), Nos. 1-2.

KÜTEMEYER, WILHELM. *Die Krankheit Europas.* Berlin: Scherkamp Verlag, 1951.

LANGER, SUZANNE K. *Philosophy in a New Key.* New York: New American Library, 1958. Mentor Book.

LASSWELL, HAROLD D. "The Data of Psychoanalysis and the Social Sciences," *American Journal of Psychoanalysis*, Vol. VII (1947), No. 1.

LEE, R. S. *Freud and Christianity.* New York: Wyn, 1949.

LESSA, WILLIAM A. and VOGT, EVON Z. (eds.). *Reader in Comparative Religion: An Anthropological Approach.* Evanston, Ill.: Row, Peterson, 1958. Read especially ERWIN H. ACKERKNECHT, "Problems of Primitive Medicine," pp. 342-53.

LETTS, HAROLD C. (ed.). *Christian Social Responsibility.* 3 vols. Philadelphia: Muhlenberg, 1957. Read especially JOSEPH SITTLER, "The Structure of Christian Ethics," in Vol. I.

LOOMIS, EARL A. *The Self in Pilgrimage.* New York: Harper, 1960.

LYNCH, WILLIAM F. *Christ and Apollo: The Dimensions of the Literary Imagination.* New York: Sheed & Ward, 1960.

McNEILL, JOHN T. *A History of the Cure of Souls.* New York: Harper, 1951.

————. *See also* MAVES.

MASSERMAN, JULES H. *See* MORENO.

MAVES, PAUL B. (ed.). *The Church and Mental Health.* New York: Scribner, 1953. Read especially GOTTHARD BOOTH, "Health from the Standpoint of the Physician," and JOHN T. McNEILL, "A Religious Healing of Soul and Body."

MAY, ROLLO. "The Healing Power of Symbols," *Pastoral Psychology*, October, 1960.

————. ANGEL, ERNEST; and ELLENBERGER, HENRI (eds.). *Existence: A New Dimension in Psychiatry and Psychology.* New York: Basic. 1958.

MORENO, J. L. (ed.). *Progress in Psychotherapy.* 6 vols. London and New York: Grune & Stratton, 1956-58. Read especially: RUDOLF DREIKURS, "Adlerian Psychotherapy," in Vol. I; JOHN GILLIN, "Cross-Cultural Aspects of Socio-Cultural Therapy," in Vol. II; JULES H. MASSERMAN, "A Historical-Biodynamic Integration of Psychotherapy," in Vol. III; JURGEN RUESCH, "Psychotherapy and Communication," in Vol. I; and ILZA VEITH, "Glimpses into the History of Psychotherapy," in Vol. III.

MOWRER, HOBART. *The Crisis in Psychiatry and Religion.* Princeton: Van Nostrand. 1961.

MUNROE, RUTH L. *Schools of Psychoanalytic Thought: An Exposition, Critique, and Attempt at Integration.* New York: Dryden, 1955.

MÜLLER, EBERHARD (ed.). *Seelsorge in der Modernen Gesellschaft.* Hamburg: Furche Verlag, 1961.

NELSON, BENJAMIN (ed.). *Freud and the Twentieth Century.* London: Allen & Unwin, 1958. Read especially JEROME S. BRUNER, "Freud and the Image of Man"; SIGMUND FREUD, "A Preface" (1917); ABRAHAM KAPLAN, "Freud and Modern Philosophy"; ABRAM KARDINER, "Freud: The Man I Knew"; REINHOLD NIEBUHR, "Human Creativity and Selfconcern in Freud's Thought"; and GREGORY ZILBOORG, "The Changing Concept of Man in Present Day Psychiatry."

NIEBUHR, REINHOLD. *See* NELSON.

NIEBUHR, RICHARD R. *Resurrection and Historical Reason.* New York: Scribner, 1957.

NIKOLAINEN, AIMO T. *Ihminen evankeliumin valossa* ("Man in the Light of the Gospels"). Helsinki: WSOY, 1941.

NORTHROP, F. S. C. *The Logic of the Sciences and the Humanities.* New York: Macmillan, 1948.

OATES, WAYNE. *The Minister's Own Mental Health.* Great Neck, N. Y.: Channel, 1961.

OLSEN, PEDER. *Pastoral Care and Psychotherapy.* Minneapolis: Augsburg, 1961.

PALOHEIMO, MARTTI. *Mielenterveys ja ihmissuhteet* ("Mental Health and Human Relations"). Helsinki: WSOY, 1958.

PARSONS, TALCOTT. "A Sociological Approach," in *Religion, Culture and Health.* New York: New York Univ., 1961.

PAVLOV, IVAN P. *Lectures on Conditional Reflexes.* New York Int. Pubs., 1928.

PEURSEN, C. A. VAN. *Leib—Seele—Geist: Einführung in eine phenomenologische Anthropologie.* Gütersloh: Gütersloher Verlagshaus, 1959.

PFUETZE, PAUL E. "The Concept of the Self in Contemporary Psychotherapy," *Pastoral Psychology,* No. 2 (1958).

PRUYSER, PAUL E. "Phenomenology, Existential Psychology and Psychoanalytic Ego Psychology," *The Christian Scholar*, Vol. XLIV, (1961).
RAD, GERHARD VON. *Genesis*, trans. JOHN MARKS. Philadelphia: West-
minster, 1961.
RAPAPORT, DAVID (ed.). *Organization and the Pathology of Thought.*
New York: Columbia Univ., 1959. Read especially MARTTI KAILA
and HANS BUERGER-PRINZ, "On the Structure of the Amnestic Syn-
drome."
RIESE, WALTHER. *The Conception of Disease: Its History, Its Versions
and Its Nature (CD)*. New York: Philosophical Library, 1953.
————. "The Pre-Freudian Origins of Psychoanalysis," in Jules H.
Masserman (ed.), *Science and Psychoanalysis*, Vol. I. New York,
1960.
ROBINSON, JOHN A. T. *The Body: A Study in Pauline Theology.* London:
SCM, 1957.
ROBINSON, WHEELER H. *Redemption and Revelation.* New York:
Harper, 1942.
RÖSSLER, D. "Psychotherapie, Theologische Beurteilung," in *"Die Relig-
ion in Geschichte und Gegenwart*, Vol. V. Tübingen, 1961.
ROTHSCHILD, F. S. *Das Zentralnervensystem als Symbol des Erlebens.*
Basel and New York: S. Karger, 1958.
————. "Laws of Symbolic Meditation in the Dynamics of Self and Per-
sonality," *Annals of the New York Academy of Sciences*, XCVI
(1962), 774-84.
RUBIN, VERA (ed.) "Culture, Society and Health," *Annals of the New
York Academy of Sciences*, Vol. LXXXIV (1960).
RUESCH, JURGEN. *See* MORENO.
RUNESTAM, ARVID. *Psychoanalysis and Christianity.* Rock Island, Ill:
Augustana, 1958.
SALZMAN, LEON and MASSERMAN, JULES H. (eds.). *Modern Concepts of
Psychoanalysis.* New York, Philosophical Library, 1962. Read es-
pecially HAROLD KELMAN, "Psychoanalysis and Existentialism."
SCHELER, MAX. *Die Stellung des Menschen in Kosmos.* Darmstadt, 1928.
SCHRÖDINGER, ERWIN. *What is Life?* Cambridge, Eng.: University, 1951.
SHERRINGTON, C. S. *Man on His Nature.* New York, Macmillan, 1941.
SIIRALA, AARNE. *Gottes Gebot bei Martin Luther.* Helsinki and Stuttgart:
Luther-Agricola Gesellschraft, 1956.
————. "Wege zum Mitmenschen," *Dokumente*, Heft 3 (1957).
————. "Ekumenian rintamalta" ("From the Ecumenical Front"), *Vartija*,
No. 5, 1959).
————. "The Meaning of Illness," *Journal of Religion and Health*, Vol.
I, No. 2 (January, 1962).
SIIRALA, AARNE and MARTTI. *Elämän Ykseys* ("The Oneness of Life").
Helsinki: WSOY, 1960.

206   BIBLIOGRAPHY

SIIRALA, MARTTI. *Die Schizophrenie des Einzelnen und der Allgemein-heit.* Göttingen: Vandenhoeck und Ruprecht, 1961. Read especially WILHELM KÜTEMEYER, "Einleitung."

SITTLER, JOSEPH. *The Ecology of Faith: The New Situation in Preaching.* Philadelphia: Muhlenberg, 1961.

————. *See also* LETTS.

SPITZ, RENÉ A. "Hospitalism," in Ruth S. Eissler *et. al.* (eds.), *Psychoanalytic Study of the Child,* Vol. I. New York, Int. Univs., 1945.

STINETTE, CHARLES R. *Faith, Freedom and Selfhood.* Greenwich, Conn.: Seabury, 1959.

STRAUSS, ANSELM (ed.). *The Social Psychology of George Herbert Mead.* Chicago: University, 1956.

SULLIVAN, HARRY STACK. *The Interpersonal Theory of Psychiatry.* New York: Norton, 1953.

SUMMERS, MONTAGUE (ed.). *Malleus Maleficarum,* translation of J. Sprenger and H. Kramer edition, first published about 1490. Suffolk, 1928.

SZONDI, L. *Schicksalanalyse.* Basel: Benno Schwabe, 1944.

TILLICH, PAUL. *Die Judenfrage, ein christliches und ein deutsches Problem.* ("Schriftenreihe der deutschen Hochschule für Politik" Series.) Berlin, 1953.

————. "The Meaning of Health." Paper delivered before the New York Society for Clinical Psychiatry, January, 1960. Psychiatry, January, 1960.

————. "On Healing." *Pastoral Psychology,* Vol. VI (1955).

————. "Psychoanalysis, Existentialism and Theology," *ibid.,* Vol. IX (1958).

————. *The Protestant Era (PE).* London: Nisbet, 1951.

————. "Relation of Religion and Health: Historical Considerations and Theoretical Questions" *(RRH).* ("Papers from the University Seminar on Religion" Series.) New York: Columbia Univ., 1945-46. Also available in *Review of Religion,* Vol. X (1946).

————. *Systematic Theology.* 2 vols. Chicago: University; 1951, 1957.

————. *Theology of Culture (TC).* New York: Oxford Univ., 1959.

TRILLING, LIONEL. *Freud and the Crisis of Our Culutre.* Boston: Beacon, 1955.

UEXKÜLL, J. VON, *Theoretical Biology.* New York: Abingdon, 1931.

VEITH, ILZA. *See* MORENO.

WALKER, KENNETH. *The Story of Medicine.* London: Arrow, 1959.

WALTERS, ORVILLE S. "Metaphysics, Religion and Psychotherapy," *Journal of Counseling Psychology,* Vol. V (1958), No. 4.

WEATHERHEAD, LESLIE. *Psychology, Religion and Healing.* New York: Abingdon, 1951.

WEIZSÄCKER, VIKTOR VON. *Fälle und Probleme*, Stuttgart, 1951.
————. *Der Gestaltkreis*. Stuttgart, 1950.
————. *Der Kranke Mensch*. Stuttgart, 1951.
————. *Pathosophie*. Göttingen: Vandenhoeck und Ruprecht, 1956.
WESTBERG, GRANGER E. *Minister and Doctor Meet*. New York: Harper, 1961.
WHITE, MORTON (ed.). *The Age of Analysis*. Boston: Houghton-Mifflin, 1955.
WHITEHEAD, ALFRED NORTH. *Modes of Thought*. New York: Macmillan, 1938.
WILLIAMS, CHARLES. *Witchcraft*. New York, Meridian, 1960.
WILLIAMS, DANIEL DAY. *The Minister and the Care of Souls*. New York: Harper, 1961.
WOLFF, HAROLD G. "The Mind-Body Relationship," *Journal of Religion and Health*, Vol. I (1961), No. 1.
ZETTERBERG, HANS (ed.). *Sociology in the United States of America*. Paris: UNESCO, 1957.
ZILBOORG, GREGORY. *Freud and Religion: A Restatement of an Old Controversy*. Westminster, Md.: Newman, 1959.
————. *Psychoanalysis and Religion*. New York: Farrar, Straus & Cudahy, 1962.
————. *The Medical Man and the Witch during the Renaissance*. Baltimore: Johns Hopkins, 1935.
————. *See also* NELSON.
ZILBOORG, GREGORY and HENRY, GEORGE. *History of Medical Psychology* (*HMP*). New York: Norton, 1941.

Index of Names

Abraham, Karl, 147
Abrams, R., 24
Ackerknecht, Erwin H., 174, 185, 203
Adler, Alfred, 147, 183
Agrippa, 162
Alcmaeon, 168
Allers, Rudolf, 174, 199
Andersen, O., 152
Anderson, George C., 172, 199
Angel, Ernest, 174, 203
Aquinas, Thomas, 54, 126
Arieti, Silvano, 147, 199
Aristotle, 30, 118, 147, 171
Arvola, 178
Asclepius, 156, 159-60
Aurelianus, C., 166

Bally, G., 147, 152, 181, 199
Barbu, Valer, 173, 199
Barge, H., 196
Barth, Karl, 137
Benedetti, Gaetano, 176, 199
Bier, William C., 199
Bliss, E. L., 25
Bogatko, F. H., 25
Boisen, Anton T., 158, 199
Bonhoeffer, Dietrich, 139, 142 ff., 152-53, 180, 183, 187, 192, 194, 198, 199
Booth, Gotthard, vii, 1-25, 35, 84, 146, 148, 150, 153, 157, 171, 174-75, 178-82, 187-90, 196-97, 199 ff.
Boss, Medard, 149, 152, 178, 200
Breuer, Joseph, 176-77, 187-88, 200
Bromberg, Walter, 154, 162, 166-67, 172, 174, 178, 189, 200
Brown, Norman O., 124, 132 ff., 191-97, 200
Bruecke, Ernst, 175

Bruner, Jerome S., 176, 204
Buber, Martin, 91, 121-22, 150-51, 157, 183, 194, 200
Buddha, 160
Buerger-Prinz, Hans, 181, 205
Bunzel, R., 182
Bury, J. B., 161, 200
Bustamante, Jose Angel, 182, 200

Calder, Peter Ritchie, 159, 200
Calvin, John, 166
Campbell, Joseph, 24
Carol, Jean, 186
Celsus, 162
Chapman, Paul, vii
Charcot, 176
Chase, Stuart, 150-51, 200
Chiarugi, 163
Cohen, A. E., 24
Collingwood, R. G., 113, 191
Cornford, Francis Macdonald, 156
Crosirer, E., 195
Cullmann, Oscar, 157, 193, 200
Cyprian, 162

Darwin, Charles, 6, 175, 179
Dean, 182
De Lamettrie, J. O., 24
Denifle, 193
Denker, Henry, 195
Descartes, 149, 170-72
Devereaux, 182
Diepgen, Paul, 161, 200
Donne, John, 22
Dreikurs, Rudolf, 183, 204
Dublin, L., 182
Dubos, R. J., 190, 200
Dunham, 186

Edelstein, E. and L., 159, 200
Ehrenwald, Jan, 163-65, 200
Einstein, 146
Eisenhower, Dwight D., 13

Index of Subjects

212

Type: Body 11 on 13 and 10 on 11 Garamond
Display, Garamond
Paper: White Standard Antique